FAMOUS MYTHS AND LEGENDS

FAMOUS MYTHS AND LEGENDS

Children's Folklore from around the World

Christine Chaundler and Eric Wood
With colour illustrations by A. C. Michael

Bracken Books
LONDON

First published 1917
by Cassell and Company, Ltd., London
as *My Book of Beautiful Legends*.

This edition published 1986 by Bracken Books,
a division of Bestseller Publications Limited, Brent House,
24 Friern Park, London N12 9DA, England.

ISBN 1 85170 005 6

Printed by Grafoimpex, Yugoslavia.

CONTENTS

Contents

Contents

LIST OF ILLUSTRATIONS

LEGENDS

THERE is perhaps no country in all the world that does not possess its own myths and legends. They have grown up about men and women who lived so long ago that their real doings and sayings have been almost forgotten, and all we have to remember them by are the old tales and traditions which we call legends. They have been handed down from father to son and from father to son until they have grown to something so strange and curious that perhaps we can hardly believe that the things they tell about ever really happened.

Whether they ever really happened or not, there is no doubt that once upon a time the people who told the stories believed that they did. They believed that giants and monsters inhabited the earth; they believed that the sun and the moon and the sky and the wind and the air and the sea were gods; and by degrees they made up stories about these gods which they thought were true stories. And they told them

to their children, and their children told them to
their children until at last they have come down to
us in the form in which we know them now, changed
and altered almost out of all recognition by their
journey through the ages.

And we have gathered together the best of these
stories and made them into a book in order to give
you a collection of the most beautiful legends that
are known in the world to-day.

The story of our own St. George is one of the
myths which have been altered so much. It is supposed to have come from the old legends about the
sun. St. George himself is typical of the sun-god,
bringing aid and gladness wherever he goes; and
the dragons he kills are the unhealthy swamps and
marshes which the sun's rays dry up and render
harmless. Later the story gathered a Christian sig-
nificance, and St. George was supposed to represent
the brave Christian soldier trampling underfoot the
dragon of sin and wickedness.

It is thought that the stories of King Arthur and
his knights have grown up around the memory of
some great king who once reigned in Wales. At first
the stories dealt only with the king and the brave
deeds of his knights; but after a while the legends
of the Holy Grail—the mysterious vessel which is
supposed to be the cup from which our Saviour drank
at His last supper, and in which Joseph of Arimathea
caught the drops of blood as they fell from His side
as He hung on the Cross—were grafted on to them, and
now they have become so mixed together that it is
difficult to say which is which. In the form in which

they are known to most of us they generally deal with the doings of some brave knight who rides forth in quest of the Holy Grail. One day you will be able to read some of the old versions for yourselves, and you will find that they vary a good deal. In this book we have kept mostly to the stories which Lord Tennyson made in the " Idylls of the King," even although in some cases he did not keep very strictly to the original versions of the legends.

What we wanted to do in this book was to give you a beautiful story, and when we found one version of a legend that seemed to us more beautiful than another that was the one we used. In the legend of King Midas and the Golden Touch, when you come to read about it later on, you will find in the old stories that what made King Midas most sorry for his silliness was not that he turned his little daughter into a golden statue, but because everything he touched turned to gold so that he could neither eat nor drink. In the old stories nobody said anything at all about the little girl. It was a long while after the tale had first been told that somebody thought that what would have hurt the king most of all was the loss of his little daughter, and the story he made about King Midas is much nicer than the original one.

One of the legends which people are not quite sure *is* a legend—that is, founded on fact or tradition—is the story of King Cophetua. Some people think that it was invented in the Middle Ages. Of course it is possible that somebody thought what a nice tale it would make for a king to fall in love with a beggar girl and marry her, and so made up the story; but it is much more likely that such a thing once really happened. King Ahasuerus, who reigned from India to Ethiopia, chose Esther, the Jewish maiden whose people had been brought as captives from Jerusalem, and who in the eyes of the Medes and Persians was nothing but a slave-girl, to be queen in Vashti's place, so it is not too much to suppose that some other king might have followed his example, and the story of his love be handed down from generation to generation, until at last it has grown into a legend.

As you read this book you may perhaps notice the likeness there is between stories that come from quite different parts of the world. Some people think that many hundreds of years ago the people who lived in Europe and the western part of Asia were all one race of men, speaking the same language, and thinking and doing and believing very much the same kinds of things. But after a time they separated. They became divided into different tribes and settled in different parts of the world, and by degrees their language became different too. Yet their old beliefs and customs did not change altogether, although, of course, they altered a little, and that is why it is—the people who think this say—that the legends of many different countries resemble each other so closely. They have grown up from the old beliefs and customs which were common to all.

Of course the stories were altered a little in different lands; sometimes they were altered a great deal, for the things which the people would see every day were put into the stories about their gods. The gods of the people who lived in southern countries were more inclined to ease and pleasure than those of the people who lived in the north. We hear more about flowers and fruit and green trees and sunny rivers in the old Greek legends than we do in the Norse ones. The gods of the Norse people were harder, rougher, and sterner. Scandinavian mythology is full of stories of fierce battles. There are legends of giants and sea-monsters, and, as you would perhaps expect of a people who lived in rocky, mountainous districts and earned their livelihood largely from the sea, their gods often take the forms of fishes, eagles, and sea-birds. Yet there are many points of likeness between the two religions. The Greek people believed in a god who was mightier than all the other gods—Jupiter. The Norse people looked to Odin, the All-Father, as their chief. Apollo was the Greek sun-god. Balder was the sun-god of the Norsemen. And both the Greeks and Norsemen tried to explain the coming of winter and spring in their myths. Proserpine, in Greek mythology, is the maiden whose advent on the earth brings summer-time, and whose sojourn with the king of the underground world for six months of the year causes the mourning earth to become desolate and barren. The Norse people believed that winter was caused by the frost giants who tried to invade the earth from time to time. The old Norsemen thought that the end of all things would come by the gradual freezing up of the earth, so when Balder is killed the whole world falls to weeping, because it knows the day is coming when the gods will be unable to stand against the giants any longer.

They are very beautiful, some of these old stories, though some of them are very sad too. Yet through all the sadness we may see shining the promise of better things. Pandora opens the magic box and lets loose all the troubles into the world; but the spirit of hope remains behind and teaches men and women to look forward to the time when the golden age will come again. Balder is killed, and Odin grows sad and sorrowful, because in his all-seeing wisdom he can discern the end drawing near; but yet he knows that the darkness and sadness will not last for ever, and that one day a new world will be born from the gloom and desolation.

All through the ages, from the very earliest dawnings of history, men have had that hope of a better time coming shining before them. And we too—although our gods are not the gods of the old Greek and Norse peoples—we too believe that one day all the wonderful things they hoped for will come to pass, that we shall see sin and sorrow and death destroyed for ever, and peace and good and happiness reigning in a new world which is but our own old world made young and beautiful again.

There are ever so many more stories that we should have liked to have put into this book if we had had room for them—stories from Egypt and India and Persia and China and many other places. But though we could not put them all into one book, yet we hope that you will like these that we have given you so well that when you get older you will find out some of the others for yourselves.

"Out flew a beautiful fairylike creature with rainbow-coloured wings"

(*see page* 4)

"The loaves had been turned into roses, red and white"

FAMOUS MYTHS AND LEGENDS

Children's Folklore from around the World

Pandora's Magic Box

LONG ago, when men first lived on the earth, they had almost everything they could wish for, for the gods who had made them gave them all the things they needed.

There was only one gift which the gods withheld from them, and that was the fire of genius, which, if they possessed it, would give them immortal souls and make them higher than all other creatures.

A servant of the gods, named Prometheus, was determined to get this great gift for men, and as he could not persuade the gods to part with any of their precious treasure, he stole some of it, and carried it down to earth.

When the gods found out that their divine fire had been stolen, they were terribly angry. They punished Prometheus by binding him to a great mountain, where he had to remain for thousands of years, until one day a brave man broke his chains and set him free.

But the gods were not content with merely punishing Prometheus. They wished to be avenged upon the men who now possessed the power which they had

B   1

meant to keep for themselves alone, and after they had consulted together, they thought of a way.

They made a beautiful woman, the first woman that had ever been made, and then they sent her down to the earth to a man named Epimetheus to be his wife.

And not long afterwards a messenger came from the gods to Epimetheus and his wife, whose name was Pandora, and gave into their charge a large carved box, which they were commanded to keep until it was sent for.

Epimetheus promised to take care of the box, and the messenger went away. But Pandora was filled with curiosity as to what could be inside, and begged her husband to open it and see. Epimetheus was shocked at the idea of breaking his trust, and refused to do as she asked, upon which Pandora flew into a temper, and husband and wife had their first quarrel.

After awhile, seeing that Pandora was still so unreasonable, Epimetheus left her alone and went out, hoping to find her in a better state of mind when he returned. But after he had gone, Pandora's curiosity grew greater and greater, and at last she began to finger the golden cord by which the box was bound.

Almost before she knew what she was doing her fingers began to busy themselves, trying to unfasten the knot. It was a hard knot and difficult to untie, and Pandora was just about to leave off trying to undo it, when suddenly it seemed to untwine of itself, and the next moment the cord dropped to the ground.

And now that the box was unfastened, and nothing remained but to raise the lid, Pandora felt that she could no longer resist the temptation to take one peep.

" I will only lift it a little bit—just to have one look,"

2

she said to herself, and just as Epimetheus came back to his dwelling-place to see if his wife was in a better frame of mind, Pandora lifted the lid of the magic box.

But alas for Pandora and Epimetheus, and alas for all the men and women who have lived upon the earth since then! No sooner was the lid opened, than out flew all the troubles that ever were in the world—all kinds of sickness and pain and sorrow and wickedness and grief and anxiety, and all the other evil things that have ever since vexed and hurt the souls and bodies and hearts and minds of human beings. For the gods, determining to be avenged upon men because of the treasure Prometheus had stolen, had filled the box full of all these troubles and sent it down to the earth, trusting to Pandora's curiosity to open it sooner or later.

These troubles flew about like horrible insects. They stung Pandora and Epimetheus with their venomous stings, and then flew abroad into the world to carry sin and sorrow and misery wherever they went.

Poor Pandora, crouched against the box which had been the cause of all her trouble, cried bitterly, and Epimetheus, filled with despair at what had happened, and finding the pain of the stings almost unbearable, began to scold and reproach her for what she had done. But suddenly, as he was in the middle of an angry, bitter speech, there came a voice from inside the box.

" Open the lid and let me out," said the voice, and husband and wife stopped quarrelling and looked at each other, startled.

" Shall I open the box ? " asked Pandora, and Epimetheus answered roughly :

" You can do as you like. Since you have done so

much mischief already, I don't suppose it matters if you do a little more. So you can please yourself."

The tears came into Pandora's eyes again at the roughness of his tone, and for a minute she thought that she would not open the box. But then she heard once more the little voice inside.

"Open the lid and let me out. Please let me out."

Then once more Pandora lifted the lid of the magic box, and this time there flew out—not an evil, horrible, ugly-looking trouble—but a beautiful fairy-like creature with rainbow-coloured wings, which shone and glittered and sparkled in the light as though they had been made of all the colours that are in earth and sea and sky.

"I am Hope," she said, as she touched the places where the troubles had stung Pandora and Epimetheus. At the touch of her gentle fingers their wounds grew well again. "And I was put into the box to make amends to human beings for all the ills that were destined to be let loose amongst them. Do not be afraid for all the evils that will come upon you. Go bravely forward, and one day you shall find the end crowns all."

And that is how the old Greek people believed that sin and misery entered into the world, and they say that if the gods had never made woman men might still be happy in the way they used to be before they knew sin and sorrow. But though it was a woman who lifted the lid of the magic box and set free all the troubles concealed within it, yet it was a woman, too, who brought hope into the world. And hope is so great and wonderful and beautiful a thing that it more than makes amends for all the evils which Pandora by her curiosity let loose upon the earth.

4

The Roses of St. Elizabeth

IN a little kingdom called Thuringia there once lived a queen who was so good and sweet and beautiful that she was loved by all her subjects. Nobody ever heard her speak an unkind word, and always she went about trying to do good to her people.

Elizabeth, for that was the queen's name, was hardly more than a girl. She had a husband who loved her very dearly, and she loved him as well. But he was older than she was, and rather grave and quiet, and sometimes Elizabeth felt just a little bit afraid of him.

One day the king rode out to hunt as usual with his courtiers and huntsmen, and after he had gone Elizabeth set out, as she often did, to visit her poor people. She took with her only one serving-maid, to help her carry the food she was taking to them; and because there was more than the maid could manage, Elizabeth herself, queen though she was, filled her apron with the loaves of bread which she was going to give away.

Now it happened that the king was not in a mood for hunting that morning, and he and his courtiers presently left the chase and turned homewards, some hours before it was his custom to do so, and Elizabeth and her waiting-woman had hardly left the castle when they met the cavalcade returning.

5

Elizabeth was overcome with confusion, and did not know what to do. She knew that her husband was good and kind, and approved of her charitable actions, but she did not know if he would quite like to think that his wife herself went round to the cottages, carrying the loaves of bread she meant to give away. She would have turned aside and avoided him if she could, but that was impossible, for already the horsemen were clattering around her, some of the grand guests looking askance at seeing the wife of their king walking about the streets in such a humble manner.

But the king smiled at the wife whom he loved so dearly, and stretching out his hand he drew her to his horse's side.

" What have you there, sweet wife ? " he said, looking down at the burden she carried, and the courtiers and guests drew nearer to see.

Elizabeth did not know what to do or say. How could she shame her dear husband before all these grand people by telling them what she really had in her apron ? For in those days people had very foolish ideas about what a queen might do or might not do, and they would have been horrified to think that a high-born lady like Elizabeth should demean herself by carrying bread to her poor people.

Elizabeth felt that she could not bear to see the scornful smiles on their faces if they saw what was in her apron, and, acting on a sudden impulse, she said quickly :

" Roses."

Directly she had said it she knew that it was wrong. She knew that she should have owned up bravely and spoken the truth, and not have been afraid of being laughed at. A crimson flush rose to her cheeks, and she hung her head, not daring to meet her husband's eyes, while the hands that held the apron trembled.

Her husband saw that something was wrong. Perhaps he guessed what the apron really held, for his voice was very grave as he bent down from his horse and said kindly but firmly :

" Let me see."

Tremblingly Elizabeth opened her apron, and the tears came into her eyes as she wondered what her husband would think of her now. But a wonderful thing had happened. There were no loaves of bread in the apron as she held it out towards her husband—the loaves had been turned into roses, red and white.

For a moment nobody spoke, then the king bent down and kissed Elizabeth tenderly.

" Go your ways, sweetheart," he said, and rode on to the castle, leaving Elizabeth standing gazing, breathless and bewildered, at the roses that she held.

It was wrong of her, of course, not to have told the truth, but she was always so good and gentle, and tried so hard to help her poor people, that God would not let her be shamed before those proud, scornful guests. So He had turned the loaves into roses and made the untruth true.

The Gods of Asgard

LONG, long ago, just as the old Greek people believed that their gods lived and reigned in the halls of Olympus, so the old Norse people who lived in the northern countries had gods whom they worshipped and believed in too. They thought that their gods lived in a beautiful country, far above the world, which they called Asgard, and there, they thought, the souls of all those who died in battle were taken to live in peace and happiness for ever.

The chief of the Norse gods was Odin. He was very great and wise, but he was often sad, for he could see into the future, and he knew that one day the world would be destroyed and all the gods would perish in its destruction.

He had not always been able to see into the future. He could see all things that happened in the world, and he knew the thoughts and doings of all men, but the gift of seeing into the future belonged only to those who drank from a marvellous well, which was watched over and guarded by a giant named Mimir.

The giants were the enemies of the gods. They had power over frost and cold, and they did a great deal of evil in the world, and the gods were always afraid that they would come one day to Asgard and conquer them. There was a beautiful rainbow bridge

8

which the gods had built between heaven and earth, and on this they had set one of their number named Heimdall to keep watch and warn them when their enemies drew near.

Heimdall could see farther than a hundred miles, and his ears were so keen that he could even hear the grass growing in the meadows, and he slept more lightly than a bird. He had a wonderful trumpet, the sound of which could be heard through the world, and when he sounded it the gods in Asgard knew that their enemies the frost giants were coming, and girded on their armour to go and do battle with them.

But though the giants were so strong and terrible, Odin made up his mind to brave the danger and go down into the land of the giants to try and obtain a draught of the wonderful water.

"For it is not right," he said, "that the enemies of the human race should know more than the gods, who are their friends."

Frigga, Odin's wife, tried to persuade him not to go, for she was afraid that some harm would happen to him, but Odin was too brave to be hindered by any fear of danger. And one day he left the great halls of Valhalla, the palace in which the gods lived at Asgard, and went to the well to ask for a drink of the wonderful water. But Mimir would not give it to him.

"No man may drink of my well," he said roughly.

Then Odin began to grow angry.

"I am no man," he cried, "but Odin, the father of all. If you will let me drink of your water I will give you whatever you ask."

"Then give me one of your eyes," said Mimir,

laughing, for he was sure Odin would not make such a sacrifice.

But Odin was willing to sacrifice even his sight to gain the wisdom which he sought. He gave one of his eyes to Mimir, and the giant, though very unwillingly, was obliged to keep his word and allow the god a draught of the water from his well.

And so Odin became wiser and more powerful even than before, and he was able to help men in their strife against evil, and by his skill prevent the destruction of the world for many long years, but even he could not prevent it for ever. Slowly but surely the evil conquered the good, and Odin on his throne in the sky grew sadder and sadder as he saw the end of the world gradually drawing near.

The Story of Beowulf

TWICE, when the people of Denmark were in distress, a hero came to their aid. The first time, when they wondered where they would obtain help, there came sailing over the sea a great ship filled with treasure and with arms, and, in it, they found a boy. Whence came the ship, and who was the lonely child, none knew; but because their coming meant succour and strength the Danes took the child of the sea as a gift from Heaven and made him their king. Scyld they called him; and years, long years, did he reign over them, and lead them to victory and conquest. Then, his work done, Scyld died; but ere he left them he told his people that his body, with treasure and with arms, must be placed in a ship and sent adrift on the sea. So, even as he came to the Danes, did Scyld leave them, and the ship bore him away, no one knew whither.

Many years afterwards, when Hrothgar, a grandson of Scyld, reigned over Denmark, distress once more came to the country. Hrothgar was a powerful king, famed in war, and he had a noble band of warriors, for whom he built a great house on the isle of Zealand. He called this house the Chief of Halls, and hundreds of his people worked in the building of it; and, when it was finished, Hrothgar gave a great feast. The minstrels

11

played, the bards sang songs of mighty deeds of valour, and the warriors quaffed goblets of mead in honour of their king, and boasted of their prowess.

The sound of the revelry swept across the marshland to Nicker's Mere, at the bottom of which Grendel, the demon of the marshes, kept watch and ward over the gloomy places. Grendel rose up from the water's depths and strode over the marsh to see what this music and mirth might mean.

He came to Heorot, as the Chief of Halls was named, and saw its towering walls, its blaze of lights, and heard its warriors boasting of their valour, and minstrels singing of the glories of Hrothgar; and the grim demon smiled as he waited in the shadows for the revelry to cease.

Then, when the warriors grew weary of feasting, and lay down to sleep, Grendel entered stealthily into the Chief of Halls, seized in his grip thirty of the greatest of Hrothgar's warriors, and carried them across the marshes to the lake; and men saw them no more.

With the coming of day, and the discovery of the raid, a great wail went up where before there had been rejoicing; here and there around the hall Hrothgar saw an empty place, and he grieved for the loss of his warriors. Little did he dream then that this was but the beginning; that for twelve years would Grendel war against him stealthily at night. But such was the case, and night after night the warriors sought their beds in fear—and those who could slept farthest from the door, thus hoping to escape the demon.

Hrothgar saw his heroes growing fewer every night, and never did one return from the lake in the marshes;

and none could reach it to give battle to the demon. Hrothgar tried to make peace—offered gifts of great value, but Grendel refused them all, and continued his raiding of the Chief of Halls until at last it stood empty, for none would sleep there.

Tidings of the great evil which had befallen the Danes travelled through the world; it reached the court of the king of the Goths, and Beowulf, a hero with the strength of thirty men in his grip, heard it, and knew that he who should save Hrothgar from the dread foe would win fame and treasure. So, with fifteen mighty warriors, the young hero set sail in his long boat and crossed the sea to Zealand.

When the long ship ran ashore, there came hurrying down the warder of the coast—whose duty it was to question all comers as to their intentions.

"Never have I seen so great a hero as he who leads you," said the warder, as he drew his sword, " and no farther shall you come until I know who you are."

Beowulf told him who he was and why he had come, and, having received permission, he had his ship hauled up on the beach. Then he and his warriors were led by the warder to the Chief of Halls. Entering by the people's door, they placed their shields against the walls, piled their spears, and laid their shirts of mail on the benches, in token that they came in peace. Then, Beowulf strode up the hall to where Hrothgar sat amongst his chiefs, and made obeisance before him, told him his mission, and received a great welcome.

There was much feasting that night in the hall of Hrothgar; warriors sat as of old and boasted of their prowess, and not the least boastful was Beowulf, who,

13

when the rest retired to sleep, kept watch and ward over the hall, waiting for the coming of Grendel, whom he had vowed to meet weaponless.

For the grip of thirty men was in the hand of Beowulf!

Once again the sound of minstrelsy reached Grendel at Nicker's Mere in his haunt beneath the lake; and he strode across the marshes under cover of the night. He heard the boastings of Beowulf, and was filled with rage. Waiting until he knew the warriors had gone to sleep, Grendel rushed at the door, smashed it open, tore it to pieces, and with eyes that shed a baleful light around the quiet hall, entered; and saw all round the beds of the sleeping warriors.

It seemed that no man watched—for Beowulf feigned sleep; and Grendel laughed as he thought of the boastings he had heard! He laughed loud and long, fearing not to awaken the warriors, because he knew that no sword ever forged could pierce him. He seized a hero—and that hero died in the seizing. He strode towards the couch where Beowulf lay—reached out his hand to take him, and in that instant the hand which had in it the strength of thirty men gripped the demon by the arm.

For the first time Grendel knew fear; he felt the grip of the hero tighten, and never before had he known such strength in a man. Then began a battle fought without weapons—such a battle as men had never seen before. The great hall of Hrothgar echoed and re-echoed with the roar of the demon, shook to the wrestling of the fighters; benches were flung to the ground, the golden goblets were trampled under foot; warriors, roused from their sleep, leapt to their feet and watched with amazement the mighty struggle, expecting to see the hall tumble about their ears—so great was the shaking of it.

> " The fair house of the world. . .
>   That it fell not in ruin, was great wonder.
>   But it was strengthened against that with bands,
>   Within, without, of iron, cunning work
>   Of smiths. . . "

Grendel knew that this warrior whom he fought was greater than any he had ever been matched against ; and though he fought and struggled and sought to escape by the door, Beowulf held him tight in his mighty grip. And Beowulf " thought his life-days of no use to any man "—because of the strength of the demon ; and yet he held fast to the arm he had caught and would not let him go. Beowulf's warriors then entered the fray, but their swords glanced off the demon, their edges turned ; only the crash of their blows increased the noise of battle and made the great hall ring.

So the fight went on until Beowulf gave the demon the death-wound ; with a mighty wrench he tore Grendel's arm from his body ; and in that moment the demon of the marshes fled from the hall and sped away to Nicker's Mere, into which he plunged ; and he knew that his days were ended.

There was great joy at the court of Hrothgar when it became known how Beowulf had dealt with the terror of the night. Where men had not dared to venture before, warriors now journeyed across the marshes to Nicker's Mere, reddened with the blood of Grendel, who lay dead in his haunt at the bottom.

Hrothgar prepared a great feast for the victor. It was held in the Chief of Halls, the walls of which, because of the great cracks in them made by the wrestling of the warriors in the night, were hung with tapestries; little but the roof remained as it was before. Once again the hall rang with the songs of bards and the boastings of heroes; the Queen of the Danes praised Beowulf, fine presents were given to him, and he was hailed as the saviour of Denmark.

Too soon the warriors rejoiced, for another and as fierce a foe as Grendel lurked outside the hall.

The feast came to an end, and while Hrothgar's warriors slept in the hall Beowulf went to another place. When all was quiet Grendel's mother rushed into the hall; there was great confusion—warriors rushed to arms to stay the monster, who, however, seizing one of the chief men of Hrothgar, succeeded in getting away, taking with her the arm of Grendel, which was looked upon as a great trophy.

Beowulf was sent for, and when he heard of what had happened, he vowed that even though Grendel's mother lay at the bottom of the lake, she should not escape his vengeance. The warriors armed themselves, Hrothgar mounted his war-steed, and, led by Beowulf, who followed the tracks of Grendel's mother, the Danes marched through the marshlands to Nicker's Mere.

The water in the lake was still reddened, dragons lay along its shores, goblins amongst the rocks. The blast of the war horn scared these creatures away, and Beowulf prepared to give battle to Grendel's mother.

Clad in a shirt of mail, a gleaming helmet on his head, and with Hrothgar's sword Hrunting in his hand

16

" The dragon was indeed a terrible beast "

"For a moment they stood looking at each other—the barefoot beggar-girl in her rags, and the king in his jewelled crown"

(the sword-edge was poisoned), he bade farewell to his friends.

"If I die, O Hrothgar," he said, "be good to my warriors, and send to my own land the gold you have given me, that my king may see that I won honour."

Then Beowulf leapt into the water to seek Grendel's mother where she lay in the dread haunt at the bottom. It took Beowulf a whole day to reach the bottom— and when the monster, who for a hundred years had lived below, saw this mail-clad warrior coming, she sprang at him; and they began to fight. The demon could not break Beowulf's mail, nor could he overcome her; together they struggled and struggled and made their way to a wonderful palace, where there was no water. Here Beowulf flung away the sword he had brought, and trusting to his own great strength, wrestled with the demon. Almost had he overcome her when she, by a trick, gained the upper hand, and held her weapon at his throat. Beowulf hurled her away, seized a huge sword (made by the giants, and larger and more terrible than any ever seen before), and with it killed the scourge of the Danes.

Then Beowulf espied the one-armed body of Grendel, and, with the giant's sword, cut off his head, and even as he did so, the blade melted away, leaving only the hilt !

Up above, the warriors waited, wondering what the issue of the fight would be. So long was Beowulf, that fear seized them that he had been overcome, but presently they saw him swimming on the surface of the lake, carrying the demon's head and the sword hilt.

With a great rejoicing, they welcomed him, and,

after further feasting and giving of presents, Beowulf
and his warriors were embarked on their long ship and
sailed away to Gothland.

Thus did Beowulf save the Danes from the scourge
of their land, the terror of their warriors.

When Beowulf returned to Gothland, his praises
were sung by every bard; and in course of time he
reigned over the land, which prospered greatly.

It happened, that after he had been king fifty years,
a dragon laid waste the land because of the theft
of riches from a hoard which he guarded under a headland washed by the waves of the sea. This fire-dragon
even burnt up Beowulf's own house, and, such was the
havoc wrought in the land, that Beowulf resolved to
fight the dragon and save his own land as he had saved
the land of the Danes.

Fashioning for himself a great iron shield which
should withstand the fire of the dragon, he went to the
headland, with several warriors who were to wait for
his return. Then he descended the crags until he came
to a river which flowed from between the mountains.
The water was hot from the fire of the dragon—so hot
that Beowulf could not dive under it without being
scalded.

He roared a loud challenge at the dragon, which
came out to meet him, breathing fire which burned
poison into the hero, who fought nobly, but less strongly
than of yore. For Beowulf was old, and his strength,
although great, was not sufficient to cause his sword to
bite deep in the hide of the dragon.

His warriors on the headland saw his plight. They
saw that the dragon was overcoming their king; but,

fearful for their own lives, they ran away—all except one, Wiglaf, whom Beowulf had favoured greatly. Wiglaf rushed down to aid his chief, and together they fought the foe. Beowulf's sword was snapped off at the hilt—the strength of his arm broke whatever sword he wielded. He seized the dragon in his strong hand while Wiglaf smote him with his sword.

So deep was the wound that Wiglaf made that the fire abated and Beowulf was able to draw his knife with which to put an end to the monster.

But the victory had been won at the price of the life of Beowulf, who lived only long enough to see the hoard of gold which the dragon had guarded.

Wiglaf sat in grief by the side of his fallen chief. The warriors who had run away came back when the fight was over and found him so, and he rebuked them with scorn for fleeing.

A funeral pile was built for Beowulf, and on the spot his people built a great mound according to the wish of their chief, and round it they chanted their dirge, praising

> " . . . Him, of kings, of men
> The mildest, and the kindest, and to all
> His people gentlest."

Thus lived and died Beowulf who, by the strength of his hand, wrought great good for the peoples of the north.

Christmas Roses

O NE night, many hundreds of years ago, a little girl was wandering in the fields around Bethlehem, anxiously looking for something. She was hunting for the lilies which grew wild in the fields, for she wanted a bunch of them for a very particular purpose.

In the little town where she lived a wonderful Baby had been born. He was only a poor Baby. His father was a carpenter, and His mother was a humble Jewish woman, and they were poor—very poor. They had arrived late that evening at the inn of the little town, only to find it full to overflowing. No—the landlord could not possibly take them in. Already his house was overcrowded—there was no room for them at all. But if they did not mind being with the cattle in the stable they might pass the night there.

Since there was no choice, the travellers had decided that they did not mind. The man had lifted the woman down from the ass on which she was riding. She was half dead with fatigue, and he had taken her tenderly into the stable and made her comfortable amongst the hay and straw, and there that very same night a little Baby Boy had been born.

There was nothing very wonderful in that? Per-

20

haps not; but that was not all. There were shepherds
watching over their flocks in the fields outside Bethlehem, and soon after the little Baby had been wrapped
in swaddling clothes and laid in the stable manger
—the only cradle His mother could find for Him—
these men had come hurrying into the town, asking
eagerly for the inn, saying that they had seen a vision
of Angels, which had told them that Christ the Lord,
the Son of God, the Saviour of the world, the King
for whose coming the Jews had been waiting and
hoping so long, had been born that night in the city
of Bethlehem. The Angels had told them, the shepherds said, that they would find the Baby lying in a
manger, amongst the cattle in the stable of an inn.

The little girl had heard the wonderful story.
She herself had seen the shepherds, as they came
away from the stable, praising God and thanking Him
for sending the Messiah to earth at last. She had
seen the peasants and the poor people flocking round
the inn to worship at the Messiah's humble cradle,
carrying with them what gifts they could find to bring.
And then the little girl had slipped away from her
home and run out into the fields to see if she could not
find something herself to take to the Baby King, whose
coming had been waited for so long. Perhaps she
could find a handful of the lilies that grew so plenti-
fully in the fields round about Bethlehem.

But though she looked for ever so long she could
not find any lilies in the fields. Perhaps it was too
dark to see them; perhaps none were out. And at last
she turned sadly homewards. She could not go to
see the little Baby without taking something with

her. When her father and mother went to worship God in the Temple, they always carried with them some offering, however humble it might be. It would not be right to go and worship the Son of God with nothing in her hand. But perhaps, if she stole very softly to the stable door and peeped inside, she might catch a glimpse of the wonderful Baby.

So, very quietly and softly, she crept to the door of the stable. The peasants had gone now; there was no one inside the rough shelter but the father and mother of the little Child. The light of the stable lantern shone through the open door, and the little girl, her heart full of love and wonder, stole up to the light and knelt down to look at the Baby King.

As she did so her eyes fell upon a patch of white on the threshold of the doorway. Surely there were flowers growing there? Eagerly the child bent down to look closer; eagerly she put out her hand and touched them. Yes, they were flowers, beautiful, pure white blossoms, sprung up in a single night from the ground where surely no flowers had ever been before!

Hastily the little peasant girl gathered them. Here was something to take to the Baby King; and with her hands full of the snow-white blossoms, she entered the shed and knelt before the mother and Baby. Poor though she was, little though she might be, yet even she, a humble peasant child, had some offering to bring to the King of Kings.

And ever since then the beautiful white flowers, which blossomed for the first time on that Christmas Day so many hundreds of years ago, have been called "Christmas Roses."

The Legend of Westminster Abbey

MANY, many years ago, when London was still little bigger than a country village is to-day, there reigned in England a King named Sebert. He was a Christian, and he wished very much to build a church for the monks who had converted him to Christianity.

At last he chose a place to build the church and monastery. It was an island called Thorney, from the number of thorn thickets that covered it, outside the walls of London, almost in the heart of the country. It was surrounded by running streams, and was so solitary and desolate that it seemed just the place for the monks to live their holy lives of prayer and meditation, undisturbed by worldly cares.

So the church was built, and at last it was ready for the final ceremony of consecration, after which the Abbot and monks would take up their residence in the monastery.

The Sunday night before the day appointed for the ceremony was wild and stormy. The River Thames, which flowed round the island, was in flood, and a poor fisherman, who had caught hardly anything during the week, went out in his boat to fish, hoping that he might at last meet with success.

For a long while he toiled patiently, casting his

nets into the river again and again, but it was all in vain. Work as hard as he would, he could catch nothing.

He was just about to give up in despair and go home, when he heard a voice calling him from the bank of the river. He rowed to the shore and found a man in a strange dress standing there.

"If thou wilt row me across to the Isle of Thorney, I will give thee a rich reward," said the stranger.

The fisherman wondered greatly what the stranger could want on the lonely island. But he said nothing, and taking the man into his boat he ferried him across the water.

"Wait here till I return," said the stranger, as he landed on the island, and the fisherman obeyed.

But while he waited a wonderful thing happened. The windows of the church that was to be consecrated the next day were suddenly lighted up with a bright light. And as the fisherman gazed with dazzled eyes, he saw a vision of angels ascending and descending on a long ladder which stretched from earth to heaven. While he was watching, so awestruck with wonder and reverence that he was unable to stir hand or foot, the stranger appeared before him. Around him shone a wonderful light, and the fisherman knew at once that he must be some saint or holy man, and he dropped on his knees before him.

"I am Peter," said the stranger, "and I am come to consecrate this church. I promised thee a reward if thou wouldst row me to this island. Thou hast toiled all night and hast taken nothing, but cast now thy net into the water and thou shalt receive thy reward."

The Legend of Westminster Abbey

The fisherman could not speak a word, but he obeyed the command and cast his net into the water, when immediately it was filled with a rich haul of salmon. Then the saint spoke again.

"Now I charge thee, when the bishop comes to consecrate this church on the morrow, thou shalt go before him with a salmon in thine hand. And thou shalt tell him that St. Peter, Keeper of the Keys of Heaven, hath already consecrated this church and monastery and dedicated it to himself."

Then telling the fisherman to pay a yearly tithe of salmon to the abbot of the monastery, and never more to fish on a Sunday, St. Peter vanished.

The next morning, when the king and the bishop who was to consecrate the church, with all their gathering of monks and attendants, came in state to the island, they were met at the door of the church by the fisherman, bearing a salmon in his hand, who told the story of the vision he had seen, and gave them the message with which St. Peter had charged him. At first the king and the bishop could not believe that the story was true, but when they went into the church there were the marks of the crosses on the walls, on the floor was the moisture made by the holy water, and on the altar they found the remains of the candles that the saint had used. And then they could not help believing what the fisherman told them.

If you were to go to the place that was once the Isle of Thorney you would have some difficulty in recognising it. The ground where the thorn bushes grew, that was once waste and desolate, is now covered with great buildings. The little streams that intersected

the dry ground have disappeared, and in their place
are great thoroughfares where motor omnibuses run and
a stream of traffic passes constantly to and fro. On
the spot where the little Saxon church once stood, you
will now find a stately abbey, that lifts its tall, grey
spires against the smoke-veiled sky of London. The
only thing that has not altered is the river that runs by
its walls, where the poor fisherman cast his net that
stormy Sunday night so long ago, and made his miraculous haul of fishes. But if you were to examine the
chronicles kept by the monks through the centuries
that have passed, and which are still carefully preserved,
you would find the record of the old legend which tells
how Westminster Abbey came to be dedicated to
St. Peter.

St. George and the Dragon

A LONG time ago, in the very earliest days of Britain, there was born a wonderful baby. On his breast was marked the image of a dragon, on his right hand he bore the sign of a red cross, and round his left knee was a golden garter.

His mother had died when he was born, and his father hired a great number of servants to look after him. But in spite of all the attendants he provided for his little son, the baby was stolen away from his home by a wicked enchantress.

This baby was St. George, who afterwards became one of the seven champions of Christendom and the patron saint of England. The enchantress who had stolen him had already in her power the other six champions, St. Denis of France, St. James of Spain, St. Anthony of Italy, St. Andrew of Scotland, St. Patrick of Ireland, and St. David of Wales. She kept these brave knights shut up in a brass tower in her castle and treated them very cruelly ; but to St. George she behaved in quite a different way. She brought him up as her own son, and when he was old enough she gave him a beautiful horse named Bayard, and armed him with the richest armour in the world. So strong was it that no weapon, however powerful, could penetrate its joints. The enchantress also gave him a sword

which was possessed of such magic power that it could
hew in sunder the hardest stone or the strongest steel.
She had hoped that St. George would help her in
her own wicked plans, but the young knight, who
had grown up brave and manly and noble, refused to
have anything to do with them. When he learnt of
all the evil deeds this wicked woman had done he
was so angry that he worked her overthrow, and finally
conquered her. Then, having set free the six champions
imprisoned in the brass tower, he started out into the
world to seek adventures.

After travelling many months by land and sea
St. George arrived in a strange land, in which wherever
he turned he saw signs of mourning and distress. As
night was coming on he knocked at the door of a little
hut which stood close by and asked for shelter.

In this hut there lived a hermit, and the old man
made the traveller welcome, and gave him food and
drink. Like all the other people the young knight
had met in this strange country, the holy man seemed
bowed down with grief and misery, and at last St.
George ventured to ask him what was the matter.

Then the hermit told him that the country was under
the power of a terrible dragon, who trampled down the
cornfields, laid bare all the fertile places, and made
dreadful havoc in the land.

For twenty-four years this horrible creature had been
the terror of the countryside, for every day, unless a
young maiden was given to him for his daily food, he
would in his fury destroy hundreds of men and women.
The king had promised to give his daughter in marriage
to the man who should slay the dragon, but though

St. George and the Dragon

many brave men had attempted to kill the monster,
they had all perished in the attempt.

And now only one maiden was left in all the land,
and that was the king's daughter, and to-morrow she
too was to be sacrificed to the terrible creature.

" After that, we know not what will happen," said the
old man sadly. " When the dragon finds there are no
more maidens for him to devour, he will surely destroy
the whole country, and we shall all perish miserably."

St. George was filled with indignation at the
thought of the king's daughter being condemned to
such a terrible death, and he determined to kill the
wicked dragon, or else die in the attempt.

So very early in the morning he rose up and buckled
on his armour, and mounting his horse he rode to the
place where the king's daughter was to be sacrificed.

Early as it was, the princess was already being
led out to her doom. She was arrayed all in white,
and she looked so pure and beautiful that St. George's
heart burned within him, and he longed more than ever
to rescue her from the cruel dragon.

Spurring forward, he sprang from his horse and flung
himself on his knees before the princess, vowing to be
her own true knight and fight for her till death. Then,
lance in hand, he rode out to meet the dragon.

The dragon was indeed a terrible beast. From
his shoulders to his tail his length was fifty feet. His
body was covered with glittering silver scales that flashed
in the sunlight as he moved, and he had two enormous
wings which spread out on either side of him. His
claws were like talons of steel, and from his mouth
came out flames of fire and thick clouds of smoke.

Nothing daunted by his dreadful appearance, St. George rode full tilt at the monster. But the dragon attacked him with such fury that the knight was overthrown at the first encounter. His spear shattered into a thousand pieces against the dragon's scaly body, and with a roar like thunder the beast turned and beat him with his venomous tail.

Blinded by fire and smoke, and overborne by the fury of the dragon, St. George fell backwards. In spite of his wonderful armour, he might have been killed in the very beginning of the fight if he had not by chance fallen under a marvellous tree which possessed such magic power that nothing evil could come under the shadow of its branches, and the fruit of which could cure all kinds of wounds and disease.

The young knight rested under the shade of this tree until he had recovered his strength, then once more he stepped out to attack the dragon. But now, since his spear was broken, he had only his sword to help him, and the smoke and fire which the dragon breathed out kept him from coming within striking distance of his enemy. Still he fought on bravely, guarding himself against the dragon's claws, until from his terrible throat the monster poured out a stream of poison which overcame the young champion, and once more he fell almost lifeless on the ground beneath the tree.

Close to his hand lay some of the fruit of the magic tree, and St. George, in his weakness, lifted it to his lips to quench his thirst. And no sooner had the juice touched his lips than he was cured at once of all his weariness and wounds, and rose to his feet as well and strong as when he began the battle.

St. George and the Dragon

The young knight knelt down beneath the tree and thanked Heaven for restoring him to health, and prayed for strength to overcome the monster. Then once again he rushed upon the dragon, determined to end the conflict, and so fierce and vigorous was his attack that at last he succeeded in getting within reach of the one vital spot beneath the dragon's wing. Seizing his opportunity, he thrust his sword into the dragon's side and pierced the creature's heart, so that he fell to the ground and died.

Then, mounting his horse, St. George rode back to the princess whom he had delivered and laid the dragon's head at her feet. He lifted the princess on to his horse and carried her back to the city, where the people welcomed them with cries of joy, and hailed St. George as their champion and deliverer.

But the king of the country, although the young knight had rescued his daughter from a dreadful death, and destroyed the monster which had been the terror of his land for so many years, did not want the princess to marry a man who was neither a king nor a prince. He did not dare openly to refuse to keep his word, but he asked St. George to carry a letter from him to another king who lived in a country a long way away. St. George readily undertook to deliver the letter, and the king having written and sealed it, he set out at once, hoping to return the sooner to marry the beautiful princess.

But the letter was to ask the other king to put St. George to death, and when the knight had delivered it, the king ordered him to be seized and cast into prison until the day came when he should be killed.

So St. George was stripped of his sword and armour, and thrown into a deep, dark dungeon, far beneath the castle. When the day came that was appointed for his death, two fierce hungry lions were let loose into his prison to tear him limb from limb. But St. George's strength and courage were so great that, all unarmed though he was, he killed both the lions before they could harm him.

The king was so terrified of his prisoner after that that he did not dare to try to put him to death in any other way. He had his dungeon still more strongly barred, and doubled the guard that stood before the door, and so for seven long years St. George was kept a prisoner. Every day his food was let down to him through a grating—poor food enough it was, just a scanty portion of bread and a vessel of water—and all through those years of captivity St. George never once looked upon a human face.

But at length, when he had almost given up hope of ever again seeing the light of day, the prisoner found in a corner of his dungeon a piece of iron. It was rusted with age, but it was strong enough for his purpose, and at last, after days and months of patient toiling, St. George succeeded in digging a passage out of the dungeon and making his way into the open air.

It was night when he escaped from his dreary prison, and under shelter of the darkness he made his way out of the city of the cruel king.

For many days and nights he journeyed, passing through many dangers and meeting with many wonderful adventures, until at last he reached the country where the princess lived.

32

St. George and the Dragon

She had remained true to St. George all through those long years of waiting, and when at last he found a way of seeing her again, she left her home and stole away with him to a friendly country, where they lived happily for a long while.

St. George had many other wonderful adventures. He slew many dragons and evil monsters, and freed the world of many horrible things; and when at the end of his life he returned to his native land, he found yet another adventure awaiting him. For a fierce dragon was ravaging England, and once more the brave knight went out to battle. This time, although indeed he overthrew and finally killed the monster, he was so grievously wounded that after the fight was over he fell on the ground and died.

The whole country, from the king to the humblest shepherd lad, mourned for the brave knight who had saved the people of England from the dreadful dragon. And the king ordered that the 23rd of April, the day on which St. George met his death, should be kept sacred to his memory for ever.

And that is the story of how St. George came to be the patron saint of England.

How Winter Came into the World

ONE of the goddesses whom the people who lived in the world so many hundreds of years ago believed in was Ceres. She had power over all the earth. It was she who made the corn grow and the flowers spring up, who covered the trees with green leaves, who made the fruits ripen and brought the harvest to perfection, and on her work and zeal depended the life of all the people in the world.

Ceres had one lovely daughter, named Proserpine, whom she loved more than anything else in the world. And Proserpine loved her mother dearly in return, and played in the sunshine amongst the birds and flowers, and was as happy as the day was long.

One day, as the girl was playing amongst the buttercups and daisies in the meadows, King Pluto drove by in his chariot, drawn by four coal-black, fiery horses. Pluto was the king of the underground world. He lived and reigned alone in a dark, gloomy land, where the sun never shone and birds never sang and flowers never blossomed all the year round. When he saw Proserpine he thought how the presence of this beautiful laughing child would brighten his gloomy palace, and springing down from his chariot he strode into the meadow where Proserpine stood knee-deep

34

amongst the flowers. Seizing the frightened girl in his arms, he carried her back to his chariot, in spite of her cries and struggles, and the next minute he was driving away as fast as his steeds could gallop.

Poor Proserpine struggled and screamed, but it was all no use. And so fast did Pluto drive in his fear lest Ceres should overtake him and snatch his new-found treasure from him, that very soon they reached the gateway to the underground world. Then, in her despair, Proserpine snatched off her girdle and flung it into a river that ran close by, begging the water nymphs to carry it to her mother. Then the gates swung to with a crash behind the king's chariot, and Proserpine was a prisoner in the underground world.

Meanwhile, above the earth the sun had set, and Ceres returned to her home after her long day's work. As she came in sight of her dwelling-place she looked up eagerly, expecting to see Proserpine come running out as usual to meet her. But to-night no Proserpine appeared. In vain did Ceres hunt for her amongst her usual haunts; in vain did she call her name in ever-increasing anxiety and alarm; and at last, in terrible fear and distress, she lighted a great torch and went out into the darkness searching far and wide, all through the hours of that long, sad night. And when the morning dawned and still there was no sign of her dear child, the poor mother determined to leave her work and search through the wide world until she found Proserpine again.

Then began for poor Ceres a long, weary, hopeless search. All her daily duties were neglected. The corn

35

died down, the flowers drooped and faded, and the grass withered away, for there was no one to look after them; and soon there arose a great famine all through the land. The people cried aloud to Ceres to return and save them. They offered up sacrifices and prayers to the absent goddess; but Ceres was far away and did not hear; or, if she heard, she did not heed, for she could think of nothing but her lost child.

At last one day, as she sat beside the banks of a river, mourning and weeping for Proserpine, the river suddenly flung a girdle into her lap; and when she came to look at it, she saw that it was Proserpine's. And as she gazed at it, longing to know what was the meaning of the message, she heard a fountain beside her, speaking softly.

This fountain had once been a beautiful maiden. She had been changed into her present form by another of the goddesses, Diana, in answer to her own earnest prayer. For the god of the river, Alpheus, had fallen in love with her, and Arethusa—that was the maiden's name—had been afraid of him, and had prayed Diana to save her and turn her into some other form. It was she who was speaking to Ceres, and she told her that, far down in the underground world from whence she had just come, Proserpine was seated on the throne by King Pluto's side.

"She is sad and sorrowful," said Arethusa. "Her cheeks are pale and her eyes are heavy with weeping. All King Pluto's wealth and richness cannot reconcile her to being separated from her dear mother."

When Ceres heard this she hastened to Jupiter,

and told him that she had found out where her daughter was hidden, and prayed him to command Pluto to give Proserpine back to her. At first Jupiter was very unwilling to interfere with the king of the underground world, but the people of the earth joined their prayers to Ceres's and prayed him to grant her petition, so that Ceres might attend to her duties once more, and save them from the starvation that threatened them because of the terrible famine.

Then at last Jupiter gave way. He said that if Proserpine had eaten no food all the while she had been held captive by King Pluto, she should be free to return to her mother.

But alas! That very day, for the first time since she had been stolen away, Proserpine had allowed food to pass her lips. She had only eaten six pomegranate seeds, but Jupiter said that he could not break his word. For each seed that she had eaten Proserpine must spend a month of every year in King Pluto's kingdom.

So for six months of every year Proserpine is obliged to live in the dark underground world, and while she is away the whole earth mourns for her. Flowers disappear, the leaves fall from the trees, even the skies weep at her departure. But when once more the gates of Pluto's kingdom fly open, and Proserpine comes back to spend six happy months with her mother, the whole earth breaks out into flower and song to greet her. The skies grow blue and smiling, the grass springs up fresh and green, the trees burst into bud and blossom, and the birds pour out their gladdest, sweetest songs. And the

time for the return of Proserpine is what we call
" Spring."

While Ceres has her daughter beside her she works
cheerfully and diligently, and blesses the world with
corn and wine, bringing forth an abundant harvest
from the earth to provide for the needs of men. But
when the time comes for Proserpine to go back to
King Pluto she grows sad and sorrowful, and leaves
her work neglected while she mourns for her lost
child. Then the people in the world have to live
upon the grain and fruit they have garnered from
the harvest, and manage for themselves as best they
can while Proserpine is away. And the six months
which Proserpine has to spend in her dark, gloomy
prison are what we call " Winter."

And however long and cold and dreary the winter
may be, yet we need never despair. The six months
will be ended in good time, and then Proserpine will
come back to the earth, bringing springtime with
her, and all will be joy and sunshine and happiness
and loveliness once more.

Why the Kingfisher's Feathers are Blue

ALONG, long while ago, in the days of the Great Flood, when Noah was in the ark with the birds and animals he had saved from perishing in the waters, the kingfisher was just a small grey bird with none of the beautiful colours by which we know it now. And this is the story of how its feathers were changed to blue and red.

After Noah had sent the dove out of the ark, he turned to the kingfisher and caught it in his hand.

"You, who have lived always by the side of the waters, will not be afraid of them," he said. "Fly out now and see if the world is visible, and bring me word again," and he loosed the kingfisher out of the ark.

Dawn was just breaking, and the kingfisher darted out into the fresh air and skimmed along above the waters, looking to see if any vestige of dry ground were yet visible. But very soon after she had left the shelter of the ark a terrible storm came on, and to avoid being dashed into the waves the little bird flew up towards the sky. She had been at rest for many long months, and her wings were fresh and strong. Her heart was almost bursting with joy at being free again, and she rose up and up, until at last she flew right into the blue of the heavens. No sooner had she touched the sky than her

39

feathers became dazzlingly blue, and now, instead of being a little dull, sombre-coloured bird, she shone with gorgeous colour.

Still she flew on, higher and higher, until at last the sun began to rise beneath her. Attracted by its brilliant light, she turned her course and began to fly downwards towards it. But she flew too near, and suddenly the feathers of her breast, scorched by the heat of the sun, burst into flame. Then she flew down to the world again and plunged into the waters which still covered the earth to quench her flaming breast.

Now at last she remembered her errand. She looked round for the ark, but it was nowhere to be seen. It had been driven far away by the storm and was now grounded upon Mount Ararat, where Noah had broken it up to build himself a house.

The kingfisher flew about the waters with shrill cries, hunting for her master. She darted hither and thither, but nowhere could she find the ark. Gradually the waters of the flood subsided, but wherever a river or a lake remained the little bird continued her search, hoping at last to find the ark again.

But she never did, and even now she is looking for it still. Her wings and back where she touched the sky are still glowing with vivid azure blue, and her breast is still tinged with the red of the flames that scorched her when she flew so near the sun. And so to this day you may see her, flying along the river banks, hunting for the ark she left so many ages ago.

Cupid and Psyche

ONCE upon a time there lived a king who had three daughters. The two eldest were very beautiful, but the youngest, Psyche, was so lovely that people said that there had never been seen such a beautiful face before. Even Venus, they said, the goddess of beauty, was not so beautiful as the king's daughter Psyche.

Venus heard what the people were saying, and she was so angry that she sent her son Cupid, the god of love, to kill Psyche. But Cupid, when he saw the lovely princess, fell in love with her himself. He could not kill one so young and fair and innocent, and he stole away as noiselessly as he had come.

When Venus found that her plan of vengeance had failed, she began to think how else she could make Psyche suffer for her beauty. She put envy and jealousy into the hearts of the girl's two sisters, so that they made poor Psyche very unhappy, and at last in despair she left her father's palace and wandered out into the world, away from all the unkindnesses she continually had to bear.

She had nowhere to go to, and after she had wandered for some time in loneliness and sadness, it seemed to her that it would be better to die than to go on living in such misery. So she climbed to the top of a high

41

mountain, determined to fling herself down on to the jagged rocks below and so end her life. But Cupid, who had seen all the persecutions showered upon poor Psyche, yet had been helpless to stop them, saw what she meant to do; and calling to Zephyrus, the west wind, he begged him to catch the princess when she threw herself from the mountain and carry her to an island far away.

Zephyrus heard his call. He caught Psyche in his arms and bore her gently but swiftly through the air, and laid her on a flowery bank in the midst of a beautiful garden.

Psyche rose to her feet in bewilderment. She had expected to be dashed to pieces on the cruel rocks, and instead she found herself in the most lovely place she had ever seen. On every side grew the most fragrant flowers; fountains played in the sunshine, and birds sang amongst the green leaves of the trees. Smooth green lawns stretched away on every side of her, and in the distance stood a beautiful palace, a place of wonder and enchantment, as Psyche found, when tremblingly she ventured to enter the great doors.

She soon found she had no cause to be afraid. Kind voices called to her to enter, and unseen hands drew her into the marble hall. There was no one to be seen, but the same invisible hands led Psyche to a table and spread before her food and wine. And when she had finished her meal they led her to a room decorated with rich hangings, and the gentle voices told her to lie down on the soft couch and rest.

So Psyche rested until the evening, and when

Cupid and Psyche

darkness fell, Cupid himself came to her and begged her to marry him and be his wife. This wonderful palace and all that was in it belonged to him, he said, and if she would only marry him all should be hers.

Psyche could not see who it was that spoke to her, but she fell in love with the god's beautiful voice and readily consented to be his wife. And after that, for a little while, she lived very happily in the wonderful palace. All day long she roamed about the lovely gardens or explored the countless rooms and long passages of the castle. Wherever she went she was waited upon by the same invisible spirits that had welcomed her coming, and when darkness fell her husband came to her, and through the happy night hours they roamed and talked together.

Only one thing marred Psyche's happiness. Her husband had told her that she must never try to see him. If she did, he said, he would have to leave her, never to come back again. Psyche promised faithfully that she would never try to do so, and though sometimes she longed to look, if only for one moment, at the face of the husband whom she loved so dearly, yet on the whole she was too happy to grieve about it very much.

At last, however, she began to wonder how her father and her sisters were getting on without her. She forgot how unkind her sisters had been, and she wished very much that she might see them again and tell them how happy she was. Perhaps they thought some terrible harm had happened to her, and were grieving about her. It would only be

43

kind to let them know she was safe and well, and at length, one night, when her husband came to her as usual, she told him of her longing to see her sisters once more, and begged him to let them come and visit her.

Cupid was at first very unwilling to grant Psyche's request. But Psyche begged so earnestly that at last he promised to send her sisters the very next day. Filled with joy, Psyche thanked him again and again, and looked forward happily to the coming meeting.

The next day the two sisters appeared as Cupid had promised they should. But instead of being pleased to see Psyche again and glad to think that no harm had happened to her, they were filled with envy of all the luxury and happiness with which she was surrounded. And they made a plan between themselves to try to take away the good things that had come to their sister.

They began by trying to make her suspicious of her husband.

"Doubtless he is some terrible monster, so hideous that he dare not face the light of day, and that is why he has told you never to try to see him," they said. "He is only waiting his opportunity, and some day, when his plans are ripe, he will spring upon you and tear you in pieces."

So well did they argue that at last poor Psyche could not keep a little doubt from creeping into her own mind. It was certainly very strange that her husband had never once let her see his face. Perhaps there *was* some truth in what her sisters said. Perhaps he was indeed so dreadfully ugly that he was afraid to let her see him by daylight, though she could not believe that he could ever mean to do her any harm. When her sisters had gone she tried to put all these thoughts away from her, but the evil words had sunk down deep into her heart, and do what she would, she could not quite forget what they had said.

When Cupid came that night, he found Psyche very unlike her usual self. She did not laugh and talk in the happy, light-hearted way she generally did ; and when her husband took her in his arms she trembled, for she could not help thinking that perhaps it might be some dreadful monster who kissed her so lovingly.

Cupid could not make out what was the matter with his wife, and at length, since he could not get her to talk to him, he threw himself down on a couch and went to sleep. For a while Psyche sat listening to his regular breathing ; then suddenly she felt that she could not bear the torture of her doubt any longer. Rising noiselessly from her seat, she lighted a small lamp, and then, with frightened steps, drew nearer to the couch to look at her sleeping lover.

Tremblingly she held the lamp so that the light fell over him, and there, stretched out on the couch, instead of the hideous creature she had half feared to see, lay the most beautiful man she had ever seen in her life—the god of love himself !

Tears of joy and happiness came into Psyche's eyes. She need not have been afraid ; her husband was no monster. Bending over the couch, she stooped

45

to kiss his forehead, but she forgot the lamp which she was still holding in her hand. As she stooped down she tilted it, and a drop of burning oil fell on the sleeping god's shoulder.

With a cry of pain, Cupid started to his feet. One glance at Psyche's face, as she stood there with the lamp in her hand, looking shrinkingly up at him, told him all he needed to know.

"Ah!" he said sadly; "you do not trust me—where there is no faith there can be no true love. Farewell; I can come to you no more." And spreading his wings, he flew away out of the open window, unheeding Psyche's outstretched hands and bitter little cry of remorse.

At the same instant there arose a terrible storm. The wind shrieked and raged round the palace, and fearing lest the walls should crumble about her, Psyche fled out into the garden. The wind caught her, and pushed and pulled her hither and thither, until at last, gasping for breath, she sank down fainting on the ground.

When at length she recovered consciousness and opened her eyes again, it was morning. The storm was over, but the palace and the beautiful gardens had vanished, and there was nothing left to remind Psyche of the place where she had spent so many happy, peaceful hours. Yet still she lingered there, shedding bitter tears for the loss of the husband whom she had learnt to love so dearly, hoping against hope that perhaps he might have pity on her and come back.

But Cupid did not come, and at last Psyche, full

of despair, not knowing what to do or where to go, flung herself into a river that ran close by, hoping thus to end her sad life.

But the god of the river took pity on her, and would not let her be drowned. He caught her in his arms and carried her to the bank, and called to his daughters, the water-nymphs, to come and help him revive her.

So poor Psyche was brought back to life, and then for many weary days and nights she wandered about the world, hunting vainly for her husband, and telling her sad story to all who questioned her.

At last one day she met Ceres, the goddess of the harvest, busy with her appointed tasks in the fields and meadows. Ceres knew Psyche's trouble, and her heart was filled with pity for the lovely girl who wandered so sadly and hopelessly through the world. She called Psyche to her, and when the girl had told her all that had happened, Ceres advised her to go to Venus and enter her service, and to try by her faithful obedience to win the goddess's favour.

" It will mean much pain and suffering for you," she said. " But except through pain and suffering no lasting happiness can come to anyone."

Psyche gratefully followed Ceres's advice, and hastened at once to the court of the queen of beauty.

When Venus saw Psyche come to her she was overjoyed. Here, at last, was her opportunity to be revenged upon the girl who, people said, was even more beautiful than she herself was. She called her attendants and told them to seize Psyche and carry her away, and set her to work at the hardest possible tasks, and if she did not accomplish them to beat her with thongs until she cried aloud for mercy.

Then began a terrible time for poor Psyche. The queen's attendants treated her very cruelly. She was beaten and half starved and set to do things which it was almost impossible that any human being could do. If it had not been for Cupid she could never have done them. But the god of love, although unseen by Psyche, saw all that was happening to her. He could not bear to see his dear wife suffering so cruelly, yet he was powerless to prevent it. Psyche had put herself in his mother's power, and nothing he could say would stop Venus from wreaking her vengeance upon the poor child. But there was just one thing he could do that might help her. He begged all the animals and insects to give Psyche whatever help they could, and, aided by them, Psyche managed to do all the work that Venus set her.

She laboured so patiently and perseveringly, and bore all the blows and ill-treatment with such meekness and gentleness, that at last even Venus's hard heart was touched. One more task she determined to set her willing slave, and then, if she accomplished that, the goddess decided to forgive her and restore her to Cupid, whom she knew was longing to have her with him again.

Venus never thought that Psyche would be able to accomplish this last task. It was nothing less than to venture down into Pluto's underground realms and ask from Proserpine, the queen of the underground world, a box containing a magic ointment which would keep whoever used it beautiful for ever.

Cupid and Psyche

When Psyche heard what Venus's last command was she was at first almost overcome with terror, for she knew something of the dangers through which she would have to pass and the dreadful things she must see and hear before she reached Pluto's kingdom. Then the thought came to her that, after all, her life was so sad and wretched that it scarcely mattered what became of her now; and, rising obediently, she set out on her dangerous errand.

But once again Cupid, though unseen, was there to watch over his wife. He called Zephyrus, who had helped him once before, to take care of Psyche and keep her from all harm. Zephyrus was only too glad to help him, for he too could not help loving the sweet gentle girl. He hastened after Psyche and told her how to avoid the dangers which she would encounter on her journey. At the gateway of the underground world, he told her, stood a terrible three-headed dog named Cerberus, who would tear her limb from limb if she attempted to pass by him empty-handed.

"But take food with you in your hands," said Zephyrus, "and when he begins to bark throw some of it to each of his heads. Then he will let you pass in safety."

Psyche obediently followed all the directions Zephyrus gave her. She threw the food to the terrible dog, Cerberus, who let her enter the gates of the gloomy kingdom, and remembering all that her friend had told her, she passed safely through the terrors and dangers of the journey, and arrived at last before the throne where Proserpine sat with her husband, Pluto.

E   49

So sweet and gentle and sad was she, that Proserpine's heart was filled with pity for her, and even stern Pluto smiled at her beautiful face as she knelt before his throne. They gave her the box that Venus wanted, and then sent her once more on her way.

When at last, after much weariness and suffering, Psyche reached the upper world again and the gates of the underground kingdom had closed behind her, she was so tired and exhausted by all she had gone through that she sank down upon the ground to rest. As she rested, she thought sadly of how her beauty must be spoilt and marred by all the tears she had shed and all the suffering she had borne. She looked down at the box Proserpine had given her, and it seemed to her that it would not be very wrong to take just a little of the magic ointment to bring back some of her lost loveliness. And she opened the lid of the box, meaning to put some of the ointment on her face.

But the box contained nothing but the spirit of sleep, which is more powerful than anything else in the world to restore lost beauty. And when Psyche opened the lid a deep sleep fell upon her, and she sank unconscious by the wayside, all her sorrow and pain forgotten.

As she lay there, wrapped in deep slumber, Cupid flew by in search of her. She had accomplished all her hard tasks now, and by her suffering she had won the right to taste love and happiness again. He bent above the sleeping girl, his heart throbbing with love and pity for her, gazing down at the beautiful face which he loved so dearly. Then, softly stooping, he awoke her with a kiss.

" Dear," he said tenderly, " all the trouble is over. You may look on me now as much as you like, for I am yours for ever, and will never leave you again."

After that there was no more unhappiness for Psyche. Cupid took her to the great halls of Olympus, where all the gods were assembled, and there she was given drink from the cup of life, which would make her immortal so that she would never die. The gods and goddesses pressed round to greet her, and Venus herself came with a smile and took her hands and kissed her.

And there, with her husband ever beside her, Psyche lived in joy and happiness for always and always, with all the pain and suffering through which she had passed forgotten for ever.

King Cophetua

ONCE upon a time there lived a king so great and rich that there was no king in the world who was greater or richer. All his councillors and his subjects wished him to marry, that he might have a son to reign after him, and many rich and beautiful maidens were brought before him for him to choose from. Even the kings who lived in far countries sent their daughters on visits to his court, attended by great numbers of servants and soldiers, in the hope that this great king would fall in love with one of them and make her his wife.

But this king, whose name was Cophetua, did not wish to marry. He did not love any of the princesses who came in state to his court, and he declared that he would never marry at all unless it were for love. And as it seemed as though he never would love anyone, his courtiers began to be afraid that he would have no son to reign after him.

But one day, as the king was looking out of his palace window, he saw amongst the beggars that stood outside his palace gate, a maiden more beautiful than any he had ever seen before.

She was dressed in ragged clothes and her feet were bare, and she looked thin and starved. But in spite of that, King Cophetua thought he had never seen a more beautiful face or a more perfect form, and as he stood there looking at her he felt his heart burn within him, and he knew that this poor, ragged beggar-girl was the only woman in the world he would ever love.

At first he tried hard to overcome his longing. How could he, a great and powerful king, marry a beggar-girl ? It seemed ridiculous. He tried to put the thought away from him, but it was impossible. Do what he would, he felt that he could not live without this girl for his wife. Rather would he resign his crown and his throne and all his wealth than let her go away out of his life. And suddenly making up his mind he turned from the window and strode to the palace gates.

When the beggars saw him coming they crowded round with pitiful cries begging for alms—all but the beggar-maid. She stood apart watching with great, wondering eyes. She had never seen anybody before who was so tall and strong and brave and wonderful as this great king, and she stood looking at him as though he had been a god. Even when the king threw a purse full of gold coins to the beggars and they scrambled to pick up the pieces of money, she did not move to get her share. She still stood with her eyes upon the king.

Then King Cophetua walked through the crowd of beggars, and came to where the little beggar-maid was standing, and for a moment they stood looking at each other—the barefoot beggar-girl in her rags and tatters, with her lovely hair loose on her thin shoulders, and the king in his jewelled crown, and his princely robes shining and sparkling with regal gems. Then the king lifted his gold chain from his neck and flung it over the beggar-girl's head.

" Come," he said. And taking the wondering girl by the hand, he led her away, through the crowd of astonished beggars who hurried to make way before him, through the palace gates, right up to the golden throne that stood in his palace hall. And there, in front of all the grand lords and ladies and courtiers who were standing round, he lifted her up on the throne and put his arms about her.

" You shall be my wife," he said, and bent his head and kissed her.

And so King Cophetua chose a wife at last, and he and the beautiful beggar-maid lived happily together to the end of their days.

The Labours of Hercules

WHEN Hercules, the son of Jupiter and the Princess Alcmena, was born, with his very first breath he made an enemy, which, to say the least of it, was very unfortunate for so tiny a person. For Hercules's mother was hated by the goddess Juno, whose hatred made her go to the extent of trying to kill the baby as he lay in the great brazen shield which was his cradle. One night she sent two deadly snakes into the palace; all was dark, and the reptiles crept into the room where Hercules and his half-brother Iphicles, were sleeping peacefully. By the way, young Hercules was never known to cry! With their eyes gleaming wickedly, the snakes reached the cradle unheard, unseen, lifted their heads over the side of the shield where Hercules was lying, and would have done their dreadful work had not the boy at that very moment opened his eyes and seen them.

Iphicles also awoke; but how differently did those two children behave! Iphicles screamed out with fright, and his cries brought his mother and father and the attendants rushing into the room, where they found Hercules gripping those two snakes by the neck, slowly strangling them!

That was the first adventure of the mighty hero of Greece; and, as you will agree, it showed that he was

55

a very wonderful youngster ! You will also be prepared to hear that the deeds he performed when he grew up exceeded those of any other hero, and it is of his famous twelve labours that I am now going to tell you.

First, however, I must make it clear how it came about that Hercules was forced to take the risks which you will see he did.

1.—THE MADNESS OF HERCULES

WHEN Hercules grew up and was married and had three children, whom he idolised, Juno drove him mad ; and in his madness he did a terrible thing : he killed his wife and children, thinking they were wild beasts ! You can imagine the horror of poor Hercules when he regained his senses and discovered what he had done ! He was filled with such anguish that he left the cities of men, exiled himself from all his friends, and asked the oracle of Delphi—through whose priestess the gods answered men's questions in those days—what he should do. The oracle, instructed by the gods, told him that if, for a time, he went and served his cousin Eurystheus, in whatever way that prince of Argos commanded, he would once again be happy ; and, moreover, that he should, when he died, become a god.

It was very galling to the proud spirit of Hercules to hear that he must humble himself this way. It was a case of adding insult to injury, for Eurystheus had, by a trick on the part of Juno, come into a heritage which Jupiter had designed for Hercules. But, had

The Labours of Hercules

the hero only known it, this service that he was told to render to his cousin was the result of the efforts of his father, who, when he discovered the meanness of Juno, had been very angry, and had made the goddess agree to Hercules becoming immortal if he performed certain great labours set by Eurystheus.

Really, the labours of Hercules, then, were to be a kind of penance for wrongdoing; and I ought to tell you that he was a man of very violent temper, and this service was designed to help him to conquer it.

The hero, when he arrived in Argos, bore the weapons which the gods had given him—wonderful weapons, every one of them. From Minerva had come the beautiful armour; from Mercury, the gleaming sharp-edged sword; while Apollo had given him a bow which drove the most deadly arrows.

He knew that he would need his weapons; knew, too, that he would want every ounce of the great strength with which the gods had blessed him, because the oracle had told him that any one of the labours which Eurystheus would set him was such that he might not come out alive!

A pretty prospect! But, once he had made up his mind, Hercules did not care what lay before him, and when he presented himself before King Eurystheus, and told him why he had come, he demanded to know what was the first labour—there were to be ten altogether, according to the arrangement.

" I'm ready! " he cried boldly.

" Go, then," said Eurystheus, " and kill the lion of the Nemean Forest, and bring me his skin! "

2.—THE NEMEAN LION

THIS first labour which Eurystheus set Hercules was
no light one, for the lion which roamed in the forests
in the valley of Nemea was a ferocious beast, who
carried off and ate whatever and whoever he liked.
His hide was so tough that no one had ever had arrows
sharp enough to pierce it; and the people were in a
terrible state of fear when Hercules arrived and an-
nounced that he was going to kill the lion.

" Don't try it ! " was the general advice given him
by the folk who were so anxious to get rid of the preying
beast. " It's no use ! "

Hercules, however, was not to be put off, and one
day he went into the forest to seek his quarry, carrying
with him his bow and arrows. He beat up the forest,
trying to make the lion come out of his den, and,
presently, he heard the monarch of animals roaring as
if in defiance of the man who had so foolishly come
against him. Hercules made in the direction from
which the sound came, and, very soon, he heard a heavy
body crashing through the undergrowth.

And he knew that the moment had come when he
must pit his strength against that of the mighty lion
whom no man yet had been able to conquer.

Dodging from tree to tree, Hercules waited, with an
arrow ready in his bow; and at last the majestic figure
of the lion stood before him, sniffing the air to locate the
hidden man, for the hero was concealed behind a tree.

A fearsome opponent did that lion look ! His mane
was flecked with the blood of some cattle which he had

just slain ; his eyes blazed furiously, his tail was lashing from side to side.

He roared with anger, and the echoes thundered all through the forest, so that the people who heard trembled with fear. But Hercules was not trembling ! He drew his bow taut, there was a twang—and an arrow sped through the air, straight for the heaving side of the king of beasts.

But that arrow, which was one that could pierce a man's armour and go through the man himself, merely hit the lion and fell harmlessly to the ground. Even the valiant Hercules began to wonder how he would fare in the combat, as arrow after arrow glanced off the tough side of the lion, which was now crouched ready for the spring. He had seen the man who had dared to come into his forest, and his anger was re-doubled at the sight of him.

Hercules flung away his bow and prepared to meet the huge form which he knew would soon be bounding upon him ; he wrapped his mantle around his left arm, and, with his right hand, seized a great club which he had made from an uprooted tree. As the lion sprang and towered above him, the hero lifted the club and brought it down with a blow which, though it broke the club and did not kill the animal, yet sent it cowering away in fear. No man had ever before struck him such a blow !

This was Hercules's opportunity ; he leapt at the half-dazed lion, seized his neck in both hands, trod upon both his hind legs, and with the strong grip for which he was famous—had not the world rung with that exploit of the baby in the cradle ?—strangled the lion, which he skinned, and from that day he wore the skin, with the jaw upon his head like a helmet, and the fore-paws round his neck : a most becoming costume, when you think of it, for such a man as Hercules !

The broken club he left upon the ground, making for himself another and a greater one with which, in the years that followed, he did many a doughty deed.

Having so far carried out the commands of Eurystheus, Hercules completed them by going back to court with the skin ; and when he arrived there and told the king of his success, his majesty, who was a great coward, was so fearful of the man who was to be his slave that he ran away !

He built a strong-room underground and forbade Hercules ever to come near him ; he was to stand outside the king's strong-room and speak through a grating !

No doubt Hercules derived a great deal of fun out of the fear of the king ; it must have helped to make it easier for him to bear the shame of serving so despicable a monarch as Eurystheus !

3.—THE KILLING OF THE HYDRA

ALTHOUGH Eurystheus was so afraid of his servant—perhaps, indeed, for that reason—he quickly found him a new task that took him out of the country. In Lerna, which was not far away from Argos, there dwelt amongst the swamps a terrible serpent called the Hydra. It had nine heads on long necks. The middle head could not be killed, and the man who would risk an encounter with the monster would have to be prepared for a number of very formidable obstacles to victory.

Hercules discovered what those obstacles were, for his second labour was nothing less than the destruction of the demon of the swamps. He was not a bit nervous, and it was a confident Hercules who rode to Lerna in a chariot, the horses of which were driven by his friend Ioläus.

When the Hydra saw the hero approaching, she, who had been wont to rush out and seize whoever came near, slunk away, and hid in her den; she feared this man, who looked so terribly strong, whose sword was long and sharp, and whose big-knotted club was such a fearsome-looking weapon.

Hercules soon devised a way to bring her out of hiding: he soaked an arrow in brimstone and pitch set light to it, and then sent it winging its flaming way into the Hydra's den.

Out came the serpent, furiously angry; that arrow had wounded her; also, it had made her den suffocating. She rushed madly at Hercules, her nine heads breathing fire at him.

Hercules met her; his gleaming sword swept through the air, and cut off one of the heads: he told himself it was going to be an easy victory. But he was reckoning without his host. Hardly had the head fallen than the startled Hercules saw two others spring up on the severed neck!

This was indeed a problem, and Hercules at first did not know what to do. He fought the serpent valiantly, but what does valour count when, no matter how you wound your foe, he cannot be killed and never loses strength ? It came to the point at last when victory was only to be gained if he had assistance ; and he called upon Ioläus to help him. His friend had really only come to watch the great fight, but he was nothing loath to take part in it.

Fighting stubbornly, Hercules meanwhile shouted out instructions to Ioläus, who, acting upon them, threw a brand into a fire, pulled it out when it was alight, and with it seared the monster's necks as Hercules knocked off the heads : this operation prevented new heads from springing up.

To make matters more difficult for Hercules, Juno, who had not given up hope of bringing him to disaster, sent a large crab to worry him during the fight. This strange enemy proved a very annoying one ; it crawled about the ground while Hercules was engaged with the Hydra, impeding his feet. Hercules, however, soon put an end to its activities : he trod upon it and crushed it to death.

Released from the attentions of one foe, who, though small compared with the chief one, might have impeded him to such an extent that he might have lost the battle, Hercules exerted all his strength to defeating the Hydra. It was no light matter to fight a foe who had so many heads, every one of whose fangs would inflict the death sting; and besides, Ioläus had to lose not a moment's time in searing the severed necks, for, so sure as he did not act promptly, the two new heads appeared.

However, at last the battle was won. The Hydra lay dead at the feet of the victor, the immortal middle head being buried beneath a huge rock so that it could never again get free. Hercules, before leaving the scene, dipped his arrows in the poisonous blood of his victim; henceforth, if these arrows only caused the slightest wound it would be fatal.

One would have thought that the great achievement of Hercules would have caused Eurystheus to rejoice; but the cowardly, jealous king, when the hero stood outside the barred door of the underground room, and told how the victory had been won, shouted out that it was not a fair fight! He said that Hercules had been sent to kill the Hydra unaided, but that he had called in the help of Ioläus.

That Hercules was angry goes without saying. How he despised the mean, weak king, who dared not look him in the face! He would have liked to run off, no doubt, and break his bondage to Eurystheus; but, remembering that peace of mind was only to be obtained by obeying the god's command, he did not go; and he was ready for the next labour.

4.—THE QUEST OF THE GOLDEN-HORNED STAG

THE third command of Eurystheus was that Hercules should capture the golden-horned stag of Cerynea and bring it alive to Eurystheus, who knew that the task he had set the hero was a very difficult one; in fact, no one imagined that Hercules could ever do it. For the stag was the swiftest animal on earth, and no man had yet been able to get near it. Besides all this, Eurystheus knew that if Hercules succeeded he would bring upon himself the wrath of some of the gods, who were very jealous of the stag; and if they had punished Hercules, Juno would have been very pleased. However, to Hercules the only thing that mattered was that the task of fetching the golden-horned stag had been assigned to him; and he set off at once. He reached the land where the stag lived, and as soon as the animal saw him, it flew off like the wind.

Then began a quest lasting a whole year, during which time Hercules was travelling over hundreds of miles of country in pursuit of the fleeing beast, which ever eluded him. But, at last, the time came when even the stag was exhausted by the man who refused to give up. Hercules came within shooting distance; he pulled his winged arrow, and sent it singing through the air.

The stag fell wounded. Quick as lightning, Hercules had reached its side, seized it, and lifting it upon his shoulders, bore it away to his master.

5.—HERCULES AND THE WILD BOAR

THUS did Hercules perform his third labour, and was ready for the fourth, which was nothing more than the capture of another wild animal. This time it was no timid stag, but the wild boar of Erymanthus, which was at large in Arcadia, to the destruction of every growing thing; and although the people of the country often banded themselves together to hunt him, they never succeeded in killing him, while they themselves seldom came out whole.

The Labours of Hercules

On the way to the scene of the wild boar's ravages among people and cattle, Hercules fell in with the Centaur, Pholus, half man, half horse. Hercules was given food by the Centaur, and after the meal he asked for wine.

Now Pholus was the guardian of the wine of the Centaurs, many of whom lived in the neighbourhood, and the wine was reserved for their own use, only to be drunk when they met together for a feast.

Pholus had no other wine, and he dared not offer this special drink to Hercules, who, however, was not content with the explanation given him.

Despite the protests of Pholus, who dreaded the anger of his fellow Centaurs, Hercules took a long drink from the cask in which the wine was kept.

Now the wine had a delicious fragrance which floated on the breeze, and told the other Centaurs that someone was drinking the wine which should only be touched when they were all together.

"Pholus has betrayed his trust," they said, and galloped, a weird company, across the moorlands to the cave of Pholus.

Hercules heard the noise of trampling feet, and, rushing out, saw the troop of Centaurs, who were crying out for Pholus, threatening him for having dared to open the cask of wine.

Then the hero realised what he had done for Pholus, and resolved to stand by him. The Centaurs hurled great rocks into the cave, and tried to force a way in by the aid of uprooted trees. Hercules stood boldly against them, throwing burning wood at them; but, finding this of no avail against the ferocious foes, he drew his bow, and shot some of his poisonous arrows.

No sooner was a Centaur struck by an arrow than he fell down dead, and the terrible execution wrought by Hercules so scared them that they suddenly turned and fled.

After them went Hercules, chasing them to the house of a Centaur, who had been the hero's tutor many years before, and whom Hercules greatly loved. The disconcerted Centaurs crowded into the house, and the owner, who had taken no part in the fight, came out to see what all the trouble was about, and to make peace.

But Hercules pressed forward, dealing deadly blows, and occasionally sending his poisoned arrows into the house, and one of these hit his old tutor.

As soon as he knew what had happened Hercules was filled with grief; he stopped fighting, and the Centaurs made no attempt to injure him while he tried to heal his friend. No arts of Hercules, no herbs, which he frantically gathered, could heal the wound caused by the arrow poisoned in the blood of the Hydra, and the Centaur died.

It was a sorrowful Hercules who went back to the cave of Pholus, who had been marvelling at the wonderful deadly work of the arrows, and was inspecting one of them when the hero returned. He handled it carelessly, and it fell from his grasp, striking into his foot and wounding him mortally.

Thus, all unwittingly, Hercules had brought death among the Centaurs. Yet, despite his grief, Hercules did not forget the work upon which he had been sent, and eventually he reached the mountain where the wild boar lived.

He was prepared to be attacked by the animal, who

in the past had rushed out at every man who dared approach. But, instead of doing so this time, the boar took fright; the towering form of Hercules, his great strength, struck terror into the animal, and away it rushed, closely pursued by the hero.

Over mountains, through valleys, and across rivers Hercules hunted the boar, and yet could not come up with it; and it seemed that here was a task which he could not carry out.

But, at last, the boar fell into a deep hollow filled with snow. This was an opportunity Hercules was determined to seize; he hurriedly made a net, and, spreading it out, caught the boar in it.

Although the wild beast struggled to get free, Hercules swung it over his shoulder, and set out for home—a strange-looking figure with his kicking, grunting burden on his back! Hercules did not care what he looked like; he had done what he set out to do, and after a long journey appeared before Eurystheus with the wild boar as a trophy.

6.—THE CLEANING OF THE STABLES

Augeas, King of Elis, had a great herd of cattle— no fewer than three thousand of them, and they were kept in one huge stable. It was a sort of large yard, with arches in the walls surrounding it, and through these the cattle were driven night and morning. It is easy to imagine that so large a place, with so many animals living in it, needed good management to keep it clean; but the servants of Augeas do not seem to have been very industrious, and the filthy state of the stables became the talk of the country ; and when Eurystheus wanted a new labour for Hercules to perform, he remembered the dirty stables.

" Go and clean out the stables of Augeas in one day," he said.

Any other man would, no doubt, have refused to obey the command ; but Hercules was not deterred because he had so short a time allowed him for so difficult a task. He went to King Augeas.

Now Hercules resolved to profit by this labour of cleaning out the stables ; why should he do for King Augeas what lazy servants ought to have done, unless he received something for it ? So he made a proposal to the king, concealing the fact that he would in any case have to do the work because so commanded by Eurystheus.

" If you will give me a tenth part of your cattle," he said to Augeas, "I will clean out your stables in one day ! "

It seemed such a totally impossible thing that, laughingly, King Augeas agreed to the terms ; and away went Hercules. He was quite confident of success, for he had been having a look round, and had seen a way by which he could perform the apparently impossible.

Near the stables was a mountain down the sides of which rushed two great torrents, and Hercules determined to use these for the work he had in hand. First he made a deep ditch from a place near the rivers to the wall round the stables. Here he cut a hole in the wall, then dammed the rivers and turned them aside from their courses, so that the waters rushed madly into his ditch, and through the hole in the wall into the filthy stables.

The Labours of Hercules

Then he made another hole on the farther side of the wall, and through it the water tore, carrying away with it all the refuse in the stables, which were thus washed perfectly clean !

7.—THE BRAZEN BIRDS

WHEN the work was all done, Hercules went to claim his reward from King Augeas, who, however, refused to keep his part of the contract ; he had discovered why Hercules had come to Elis, and was angry at having been foolish enough to offer to pay for what would have been done for nothing !

Hercules was wroth with the dishonest king ; and when his term of service with Eurystheus was over, he led an army into Elis and utterly defeated Augeas in a great battle, during which the king was killed. It seemed that Hercules was fated in the task, for, when he returned to Argos and told Eurystheus what had happened, the king would not allow the labour because the hero had come to an arrangement with Augeas to be paid for the work.

Perhaps it was because the anger of Hercules was very terrible that King Eurystheus soon found him another task. This time it was to drive away from the marsh of Stymphalus a swarm of birds which were a terror to man and beast. These birds had brazen beaks and claws and wings, and they would swoop down, kill any whom they saw, and devour them ! They were, indeed, a terrible pest, and no one could drive them away from the marsh where they had taken refuge a long time before from the wolves which had been used to prey upon them.

One reason why the birds were so secure in their retreat was that the marsh of Stymphalus would not bear the weight of a man; it was one vast stretch of yielding mud, and engulfed whoever tried to penetrate its recesses.

Hercules, after having inspected the marsh, which he saw was literally covered by the birds, realised that he was face to face with a very difficult task, and that unless he received help, he could not possibly succeed.

Help came to him from his friend, the goddess Minerva, who gave him a great horn rattle with instructions how to use it.

That was indeed a very queer sort of weapon with which to fight the birds, but it was a very effective one. Hercules went up on to the top of a mountain near the marsh and, standing there, shook his rattle with all his might. Such a noise it made! The people in the neighbourhood put their fingers in their ears to deaden the sound; and the birds in the swamp, startled as they had never been before, left their resting-places and rose high in the air—a great swarm which hid the light of the sun!

This was just what Hercules had expected. He drew his bow, and shot his poisoned arrows at the birds. Hercules had never shot so rapidly in his life as he did now, and great numbers of the wild birds fell to the ground dead. Those which escaped flew on and on, and never again did they dare go near the swamp.

Thus ended the sixth labour of Hercules, who was soon off on another one.

The Labours of Hercules

8.—THE CRETAN BULL

NEPTUNE, the sea god, had once sent to Minos, King of Crete, a beautiful bull—the like of which Minos had never before seen—that it might be offered as a sacrifice. But the king was so charmed with the size and the beauty of the bull that he resolved to keep the animal for himself, and try to deceive Neptune by offering another animal as a sacrifice.

Neptune, however, discovered the trick, and, as a punishment to Minos, he drove the bull mad; so that, far from being a beast worth keeping, it became a terror throughout the island. It spread havoc wherever it went; and Minos was sorry that he had disobeyed the god's commands.

No man, however, had succeeded in taming the mad bull, and the task of doing so seemed to Eurystheus a sufficiently difficult one for him to set Hercules as his seventh labour.

The hero left Argos, and sailed away to Crete, where he told King Minos the reason of his visit.

Minos was overjoyed that someone had at last summoned enough courage to try to capture the bull; his only regret was that it might not be killed, because Neptune had forbidden Hercules to do more than capture it.

However, Hercules assured Minos that, when once he had the bull safe, he was going to take it off to Greece : that was better than nothing !

Hercules went seeking the bull, and it was no difficult matter to follow it, for its travels were marked

by the ravages it had caused. The maddened brute
was a fearsome-looking antagonist ; anyone watching
Hercules and the bull would have said that there was
no hope of the man coming out victor, for the beast
made ugly rushes at Hercules, the thunder of its hoofs
upon the ground sounding like thunder-claps. It seemed
to breathe fire, it bellowed angrily, and its great
horns swished about like lances! Hercules, sure in his
own strength and skill, could easily have killed him.
Would not one of those poisoned arrows send the
bull headlong to the ground ? But Neptune had forbidden that course, and the hero had to dodge the
rushes of the bull, skipping aside with great agility,
and trying to seize hold of the horns as the animal
dashed by.

At last, with a bound, Hercules had seized the
horns. Then began a terrific wrestle between man
and beast ; but, strong though the bull was naturally,
and stronger because of its madness, Hercules won.
He dragged his captive down to the shore, lifted it
bodily upon his shoulders, and put it on board the
waiting ship, where it was bound fast and carried
away to Argos, where everyone marvelled at the
prowess of the hero. It would have been well for
Greece had Hercules been allowed to kill the bull
he had caught, for it got loose, and for many years
ravaged Greece as it had ravaged Crete ; it was not
until another hero, Theseus, went out to fight it that
it was killed.

Hercules, however, had done the work given him
by Eurystheus, and it was no fault of his that the bull
remained as a scourge.

72

The Labours of Hercules

9.—DIOMEDES' HORSES

DIOMEDES, king of the people called Bistones, in Thrace, had a large number of beautiful mares, which he fed on human flesh. He made it a rule that any strangers who came into Thrace should be taken prisoner, and well fed until they were fat enough, and then be thrown into the mangers of the mares.

To punish Diomedes for his cruelty, and, no doubt also to provide Hercules with a task in which he might possibly lose his life, Eurystheus sent the hero to Thrace to capture the animals and bring them to Greece.

Hercules, on this occasion, took a number of friends with him, for he realised that the work was likely to prove difficult; and with them he went to Thrace, called on the king, and commanded him to give up the mares.

Naturally, Diomedes was not willing to do this; and, indeed, he saw in the men from Greece many good meals for his horses.

Hercules, therefore, resolved to take the mares by force. He waited for a favourable opportunity, then suddenly swooped down upon the stablemen who were looking after the animals, defeated them, and drove the mares to the shore, where his ship was riding at anchor.

All seemed well, but really it was not so. Diomedes had heard of what had happened. Angry and furious, he gathered his soldiers together and hurried after Hercules, reaching the coast when the Greeks were about to embark the mares.

73

Naturally, there ensued a great battle, during which Hercules placed his friend Hermes in charge of the horses. The fight resulted in a crushing defeat of the Bistones, and the death of their king.

Then, because Diomedes had been so cruel, Hercules threw his body to the mares as a punishment. A wonderful thing happened immediately after that: before, the animals had been wild; now, they were tamed, and were easily got on board the waiting ship.

But although he had been so successful Hercules had to mourn the loss of his friend Hermes, whom the mares had killed; and in honour of him the hero stayed awhile and built a town, which was named Abdra.

When this was done Hercules embarked, and sailed away to Greece, with his cargo of beautiful horses. The very sight of the animals, however, although they were now tame, filled Eurystheus with fear; he remembered what their reputation was, and he let them escape !

Off they went like the wind, into the forests, where wild beasts preyed upon them till not one was left.

10.—THE GIRDLE OF HIPPOLYTE

MARS, the god of war, once gave to Hippolyte, the queen of the Amazons, a girdle of gold and precious stones—the best girdle in the world, and coveted by many. But as the Amazons, a strange people, consisting only of women, were great warriors, brave, and skilled in the use of arms, no one had dared to rob the queen of her ornament.

74

The Labours of Hercules

Admete, the daughter of Eurystheus, however, was a very vain and covetous young miss, and she told her father that nothing in life would please her better than to possess the girdle of the queen of the Amazons; and as the king had in Hercules a servant who was not only bound to do his bidding, but who had, so far, always been successful, it seemed to him that it was possible to get the girdle. In any case, Eurystheus would not run any danger!

When Hercules heard what he was to do he made preparations. He realised that if he was to be successful he must have aid against the Amazons, who were not likely to part with Mars' gift. So he sent messengers far and wide, calling for volunteers to accompany him to the land of the Amazons; and the young men of Greece, bold and fearless, and always willing to go to war, especially when led by one who knew how to wrest victory from powerful foes, flocked around him.

When he had sufficient followers, Hercules embarked on a large ship and sailed away on his next venture, which was to be greater than he had imagined it would be.

For one thing, he was held up at Paros by a quarrel with the sons of Menos, and he had to give battle to them, in which two were killed.

Having settled that little matter he continued on his way, but by now the fame of Hercules was such that kings would have given him a great deal to have had him as general in their armies; and it was his fame which prevented him going on to the land of the Amazons for some time.

When he arrived in the land of Thysia, the king,

Lycus, who was at war with another people, asked Hercules to join forces with him. The hero, nothing loath, because he believed that Lycus was in the right, agreed, and in the fighting that followed the enemy was utterly defeated, and a part of the country fell under the sway of Lycus. In honour of the friend who had so nobly helped him, the king named the district after Hercules.

At last Hercules was free to continue his voyage, and in due time, having crossed a great sea, which he named the Euxine, he arrived at the port of the land of the Amazons.

When he presented himself to Hippolyte, she naturally wanted to know why he had come to her country with an armed force.

" I have come," said Hercules, " for the girdle which Mars gave you; Eurystheus has sent me for it ! "

The news of the exploits of the hero had reached Hippolyte, and she knew that what Hercules set out to do was sure to be done; if Eurystheus wanted the girdle and had sent Hercules to fetch it—then the girdle would be taken to the king. There was no doubt about that !

So, after thinking the matter over, the queen came to the conclusion that it would save trouble to give the girdle to Hercules. All would have been well but for Juno's realising that one of the labours of Hercules was likely to be done without his having to fight. This was quite contrary to all the desires of the goddess; she had been willing for Hercules to gain immortality, to make up for having lost his inheritance, if he could perform all the tasks set him; but she was not at all willing for him to have even one easy task !

The Labours of Hercules

So, while Hippolyte was making up her mind, Juno, taking on the form of an Amazon, went amongst the fighting women.

" This man of Greece," she said, " has not come merely to get the girdle of Mars ! "

" What, then, has he come for ? " the women demanded, for every one of them was interested in the visit of the far-famed Hercules.

" To kidnap the queen ! " said Juno.

The news spread like wildfire throughout the land, and Juno was well pleased with her plotting when the Amazons gathered in great numbers, every one of them mounted on a horse, and spurred to the queen's palace.

There arose a great turmoil ; they were astonished to hear that the queen was willing to give up the girdle, but they refused to allow her to do so.

So the queen could not do as she wished ; and when Hercules heard what had happened—that the women warriors of Hippolyte were gathered in force about the queen—he immediately jumped to the conclusion that she had betrayed him—that she had broken the promise she had made that the girdle should be handed over.

The result of Juno's interference was that the Amazons and the Greeks met on the field of battle ; there was a terrible fight, the Greeks fighting apparently against odds, for the Amazons were in large numbers and were all on horseback, while the men were on foot ; but Hercules, by his skilful handling and his fearless example, overcame the foes, who, although they were women, were by no means to be despised ; and Hippolyte was defeated.

Thus, by war, Hercules gained what he would have received by peace but for the enmity of Juno. The girdle was in his possession !

Leaving the field of battle, Hercules and the remainder of his men embarked on their ship, turned her towards Greece and ploughed the seas, a happy band of warriors who had succeeded in their mission.

But the way home was to provide Hercules with an opportunity for chivalry. He cast anchor at the city of Troy, and called upon Laomedon, the king, whom he found in a dreadful state of panic. Laomedon had offended Apollo and Neptune. Some time before the two gods had paid a visit to Troy, and the king, who did not know who they were, had come to an arrangement with them to build him walls that it would be beyond the power of man to destroy.

Apollo and Neptune set to work : they laboured at the walls of Troy, which, when completed, were strong enough to satisfy Laomedon ; but when the gods came and asked for their payment, the king, thinking them to be only ordinary men, broke his word. He felt that he was so powerful that he need not trouble about what they thought or did ; for, even supposing them to be two heroes who could call around them a big army, were not the walls they had thrown around Troy strong enough to withstand any enemy ?

He scorned them. And the gods punished him.

No light punishment, either, was it that they sent upon him ! A great monster arose out of the sea and ravaged the country, until no Trojan dared to go out of the city ; the fields lay uncultivated, famine was upon the place, panic was widespread ; and the people

The Labours of Hercules

turned upon Laomedon, who, afraid of the consequences and realising now that he had done wrong, went to the oracle and sought advice.

" Chain your daughter to a rock on the seashore," said the oracle, " and the monster will come up out of the sea and devour her. Thus shall the land be saved from the wrath, for afterwards the dragon shall not ravage."

Laomedon shivered when he heard the words of the oracle; his daughter Hesione was the apple of his eye, and he tore his hair when he realised that his own deeds had called for so great a sacrifice; yet he knew it was absolutely necessary for him to offer his daughter upon the altar of her country's need.

So to the seashore was the weeping Hesione led; and the waves broke all around the rock to which she was chained as she waited for the coming of the dragon.

It was at this time that Hercules appeared on the scene; it did not take him long to find out the reason for the binding of so beautiful a maiden, and when he knew, he said :

" Do not fear, Laomedon ! I will save your daughter and kill the monster."

The very simplicity of the hero's words, and the glory of his fame, calmed the anxious and grief-stricken king, who promised him that if he were suc essful he should have as a gift the horse which Jupiter had given to the Trojan king : the fastest horse in the world, and much coveted.

So off to the shore went the hero, where he waited by the side of the now hopeful maiden, who rejoiced in having so valiant and conquering a champion as the famous Hercules; and when the dragon, eager for his prey, arose out of the sea, imagining, no doubt, that he would have two meals instead of one, Hercules met him, and there was a great combat. But nothing could stand against the skill and the strength of the hero, who finally killed the monster and carried Hesione back to her father. Never was there so mean and untrustworthy a man as Laomedon! Even as he had broken his word to Apollo and Neptune, and so brought great trouble upon the people, so he now refused to give Hercules the horse he had promised!

And never was man so angry as Hercules at the treachery. He could not stay to punish the king, but he sent word, saying:

"Some day I shall return to Troy and then shall Laomedon know what it means to break troth with Hercules!"

And if Laomedon did not tremble on his throne, then he was braver than he was mean.

Leaving Troy in disgust and anger, Hercules sailed off and eventually reached Greece, where, as you may suppose, the sight of the girdle filled Eurystheus and his covetous daughter with delight.

11.—THE CATTLE OF KING GERYON

GERYON, the terrible three-headed king of Erytheia, was the possessor of a herd of beautiful cattle, and he was as jealous of them as Diomedes had been of his horses. He would allow no one to kill them, and to prevent anybody raiding the herd, he had a watch-dog named Orthrus. More than one head seemed to be the fashion in Erytheia, for Orthrus had two heads; and he was so strong, that in the fights he sometimes had with beasts of prey who prowled about the meadows, he was always the victor; he could tackle two foes at once and kill them both.

Because of the risks that would attend any attempt to obtain Geryon's cattle, Eurystheus made that the tenth labour; and he rubbed his hands as he thought that he had got rid of the servant who struck terror into his very soul every time he returned successfully from expeditions which had seemed to promise disaster.

With his big club and his bow and arrows, Hercules set off for Erytheia, crossing the desert of Libya. The blazing sun poured down upon the arid waste of sands, which the galloping horses kicked up in great clouds.

Hercules, who was all alone on this adventure, was very cross with Apollo, the sun-god, for driving his chariot through the sky, and thus causing the terrible heat; and he called upon Apollo to stand aside and not allow his burning rays to fall upon him!

Such presumption on the part of a mortal amused Apollo, who, laughing scornfully, said:

" The road is mine and——"

Hercules was not in a nice mood; he was furious—heat does make people very short-tempered!—and he drew his bow, aimed straight at Apollo, and would have shot—forgetting that, because he was a mortal, he could not hurt the god. The more angry Hercules became, the more amused was Apollo.

After a time, filled with admiration for the courage displayed by the hero, Apollo told him that he would help him on his way to the island of Geryon by lending him a golden ship. It is said that Hercules himself made the strait between Europe and Africa by tearing a gap in the mountains which allowed the waters of the Middle Sea to unite with the ocean beyond. And, to-day, the cliffs on each side of the Straits of Gibraltar are called the Pillars of Hercules.

But although Apollo had given him the ship of gold, which ploughed the sea between Africa and Europe, Hercules was not to find his passage easy. One of the sea-gods troubled the waters, and raised a great storm; all was black except for the lightning flashes which cut through the sky and showed up the ship gleaming golden against the dark background of clouded sky and tumbling waves.

Even as he had been angry with Apollo for the burning heat of his rays, so now was Hercules furious with Neptune, who was scornfully looking on. The hero, standing up in the rocking ship, drew his bow and threatened that if the storm did not abate, he would shoot! Neptune was so frightened that he calmed the waves immediately! At last Hercules arrived at Erytheia, and, landing, was attacked by the dog Orthrus, which, after a terrible fight, was killed by the hero. Then Eurythion, who was one of the keepers of the cattle, and allowed the animals to eat men, was also encountered, and fell at the hands of Hercules, who then found himself in possession of the wonderful herd.

He gathered the beasts together, and drove them down to the shore; but Geryon, to whom news had been carried that a robber had raided his fair meadows, came out to give battle, and to prevent the cattle being embarked.

Hercules met him : he was afraid of no man, even though that man had three heads, and could use several weapons at once ! He drew out his bow, fitted an arrow, and loosed it at the hideous monster, who went tumbling to the ground, dead.

Even although he had been so successful, Hercules had by no means completed his task ; the journey to the court of Eurystheus was a long one, and the herd large.

He got the cattle over to Spain and began to drive them through the country, over rivers, across mountains. Everywhere the people flocked to see the far-famed hero who had raided the farm of Geryon, and many were the jealous eyes cast upon the beautiful cattle. In Liguria, indeed, the chiefs resolved that they would take them from Hercules, even as he had taken them from Geryon.

So, gathering their warriors together in thousands, they suddenly swooped down upon Hercules as he was driving the herd ; and a great fight began. At first, the Ligurians got to close quarters, but the mighty club of the hero, swinging swiftly round and round, and, as it were, making a moving wall, sent the attackers hurrying back—that is, all who were not left dead upon the ground. Discretion made the foes keep at a distance now, but they had not yet given up all hope of defeating Hercules. Showers of arrows were shot at him, and a rain of big stones also worried him, and as he had his herd to look after, he might have fared ill if Jupiter had not come to his assistance.

He had used up all his arrows, when, suddenly

from the heavens, there came a deafening noise—and the hero's enemies, who were confident that Hercules would have to give in, were scattered in terror as a shower of tremendous stones came hurtling down upon them : Jupiter had come to the rescue !

Many of the Ligurians were killed, and the rest fled in dismay, when Hercules, picking up the great stones as though they were pebbles, flung them one after another into the mass of his foes.

Hercules won that battle ; and to-day you can see the battlefield in Provence, where the big stones still lie !

After this adventure Hercules went on his way, driving the cattle over the Alps, and cutting himself a road through the ice and snow. Now through the bleak mountains, where the animals were often hungry ; now through verdant valleys, where food was plentiful, the cattle-drover held on his way, passing down the long limb of Italy until he came to the Tiber, where the city of Rome now stands. Here, under Mount Aventinus, was a cave, in which lived a giant named Cacus, an even more fearsome person than Geryon, for he breathed out fire which consumed everyone who came near— not that many people dared approach the cave ! Cacus would go out and trouble peace-loving folk, stealing their cattle, and burning up any who tried to oppose him.

What he had done to the people near Mount Aventinus he thought he could do to Hercules, when he saw the hero coming along with the beautiful herd. That evening, when Hercules camped for the night, Cacus waited for his opportunity, and, while Hercules slept, crept out and drove into the cave some of the best of the cattle. He was a cunning man, Cacus, for, so that Hercules should be put off their trail, he dragged the animals in by their tails; and the footprints made it seem that the animals were going *out* of the cave instead of *in !*

Cacus chuckled to himself as he thought of the trick he had played upon Hercules, and when the morning came, and the hero, missing some of his cattle, began to search for them, the giant rubbed his hands with glee, for Hercules had not the least suspicion that the marks near the cave were the clues to their whereabouts.

At last Hercules, imagining that some of them had strayed during the night and had got lost, had to go on without them.

But while he was driving his herd along the foot of Mount Aventinus, one of the animals lowed; and instantly the cattle in the cave, recognising the voice of their companion, answered !

The anger of Hercules was terrible to see : he rushed up to the cave, the mouth of which was blocked with great rocks, and he tore them down in fury, until the dark recesses of the cave were before him. Inside, he could hear his cattle lowing; and caring not for whoever might be within, he plunged into the inky blackness.

Cacus was waiting for him. There was no escape for the giant, and, confident in himself because of his fiery breath, he rushed at Hercules, breathed fire upon him—but breathed in vain.

Here was a man who cared not for fire, and, while the giant yelled in anger and in pain, Hercules be-

laboured him with his mighty club until Cacus dropped
to the ground, dead.

Recovering his stolen cattle, Hercules once more
continued his journey. He had many more adventures
before he reached Greece, but as most of them were
very much like these others, we will not bother about
them, but hurry on with Hercules to his own land.
One adventure, however, we must give, and that was
when Juno, on the arrival of Hercules in Thrace, determined to make it impossible for him to deliver the herd
to Eurystheus.

She drove the cattle mad! The frenzied herd ran
away, bellowing loudly, so that the people who heard
fled in terror from their vicious rush. Poor Hercules
realised that he had indeed a hard task before him,
for his cattle were going madly across country, and there
were many straying to either side. He gathered the
stragglers, and set off in pursuit of the fleeing animals.
They raced on and on, across plains and through rivers—
at one place where the waters were deep Hercules had to
hurl big rocks into the river to make himself a road.

Gradually, as the miles were covered, he drew
nearer and nearer, and regained his cattle one by one,
until by the time he reached the shores of the Hellespont
he had them all together again.

Such were some of the trials and troubles of Hercules during his journey back to Argos, which in course
of time he reached, and handed over his prize to
Eurystheus, who, when he heard of all that had happened, wanted to get rid of the hero as quickly as
possible. Yet, Eurystheus and Juno were disappointed
that Hercules had been successful in every one of the

ten labours, and that, although he had been often in peril, he had come through alive. So, pretending that because Hercules had had help during two of his exploits, Eurystheus told him that he should not be released from his service until he had carried out two further tasks to make up for them.

The first of these was to be the bringing of the golden apples of the Hesperides.

12—THE APPLES OF THE HESPERIDES

NEAR the mountain where Atlas stood with the weight of the heavens upon his shoulders, there was a garden where some beautiful maidens had charge of a number of golden apples, which Juno had received as a wedding present. These precious fruits were held in high esteem, and to aid the Hesperides, as the maidens were called, a many-headed dragon was set to keep watch night and day, so that no man should steal them. As the apples really belonged to Juno, who took such care to have them guarded, it seemed unlikely that Hercules would succeed in bringing them to his master!

As a matter of fact, although Hercules was nothing loath to go in quest of them, he was in a very awkward position : he did not know where the garden of the Hesperides was. He made many inquiries of people whom he thought should know; and he met many adventures while doing so, and had to give battle to several foes who were made by Juno to quarrel with the man who would seek the golden apples.

After a time Hercules came to a river on the banks of which sat three water-nymphs. Now, Hercules seldom met anyone but what he asked, "Do you know where the garden of the Hesperides is?" and so as soon as he saw the water-nymphs he put his question to them.

As it happened, the three maids of the water knew something that was to prove useful to the hero.

"Go down to the sea," they said, "and ask Nereus, the sea-god, to tell you the way to reach the garden; he knows!"

You may be sure that Hercules was very pleased to hear this, and, thanking his fair friends, he hurried away to the sea-shore.

The only thing that worried him was as to how he would be able to find Nereus; and you can imagine how pleased he was when, coming within sight of the gleaming sandy beach, he saw an old man lying fast asleep.

"Nereus!" Hercules muttered to himself, and the next instant had bounded to the side of the sleeping sea-god and was shaking him till his head seemed likely to tumble off!

Such rough handling awoke Nereus, who looked with astonishment at the towering man holding him in a grip of iron; and he was more than startled when Hercules demanded of him the way to the garden of the Hesperides.

Now, Nereus could be a most annoying person when he made up his mind to be. He did not want to give the bullying hero the information asked for, and he tried all manner of troublesome ways to get free of the vice-like grip in which he was held. He could change himself into whatever shape he liked, and it was a good job for Hercules that he was brave and strong; for queer things happened!

Instead of Nereus, he found himself holding a barking dog, which snapped and snarled and tried to escape; then, when he found he could not get free, Nereus changed himself into a gigantic bird which strained on the wing—and could not fly because Hercules kept his grip. Snakes and giants and wild animals—anything that Nereus thought would frighten Hercules—were the forms that the sea-god assumed; but he might just as well have given in at the beginning, for the hero never loosed his hold, and Nereus at last had to give up the struggle and tell Hercules as much as he knew.

"I don't know the way myself," he said, "but, if you go to Prometheus in the mountains far away, where Apollo sets out in his chariot, he will be able to tell you the way."

So off went Hercules to the east; and after a long journey he came to where Prometheus was chained to a rock. You have already been told how Prometheus was kept a prisoner, with a big eagle always preying upon him, because he had stolen fire from heaven when Jupiter would not let man have fire.

Although, of course, Hercules did not know it, before he could attain immortality he was to set Prometheus free. Knowing only that the chained prisoner, who for many years had suffered great agonies, could help him, Hercules, as soon as he saw the big eagle, attacked it, and after a fierce struggle killed it. After that it did not take long to release Prometheus, who, grateful to his rescuer, told him that Atlas, who held the heavens on his shoulders, knew just where the garden of the Hesperides was, and the way to reach it.

Off went Hercules again; and during his journey fell into a stranger adventure than any he had yet met with. He arrived in the land of the pygmies, who, in constant dread of being devoured by the cranes who swept through the air, and of being overwhelmed by their larger and more powerful neighbours, had accepted an offer made to them by the giant Antæus, who was willing to be their protector. When the pygmies saw the great form of Hercules coming, with his big club swinging in his hand, they rushed to Antæus and told him. They felt that only he could save them, and they had good ground for thinking so, because Antæus was a queer sort of person, seeing that no matter how tired or battle-weary he was, as soon as any part of his body touched earth, his strength was renewed !

Hercules, of course, knew nothing of this, and when Antæus came forward to challenge him, he met him boldly; and then the pygmies standing round witnessed a terrible struggle between the two men. What a fight that was, to be sure ! Hercules, who had won so many combats, realised that he had met a foe who seemed likely to overpower him; but just when he felt that the end had come, he discovered the secret of the strength of Antæus—he must keep him from touching earth !

Waiting his opportunity, Hercules suddenly rushed at Antæus, seized him in his strong arms, and using every ounce of strength left, lifted him high in the air, where, despite his struggling, he kept him. Moment by moment the giant lost strength; his struggles became weaker and weaker; and the steel grip of Hercules began to squeeze the life out of him, and, at last, Hercules knew that all was over. When Antæus was quite dead, he flung him away, to the alarm of the pygmies, who had been so sure of their protector's power to shield them.

Hercules was tired after his exertions, and was soon fast asleep; and taking advantage of this, the pygmies attacked him. But their arrows—thousands and thousands were shot at the sleeping hero—only glanced off; they set fire to his hair, but waking up, he soon put that out, and seeing that they could not kill him with arrows, or burn him with their fire, the pygmies trembled for their own lives.

However, Hercules scorned to hurt such tiny creatures, and, anxious to be on his way, left their country, and after many adventures, both by land and sea, a golden ship carried him across the water to where Atlas held up the heavens, and he came to the edge of the world. Here a mighty mountain reared its cloud-capped head, and a very giant of giants stood there with a weight upon his shoulders that seemed to be too great for anyone to bear.

It was Atlas.

Bowed down beneath the weight of his burden, he was a pathetic figure—who dared not for one moment take à rest from his labours, because if he did the heavens would fall.

Hercules, when he saw Atlas, hoped that the end of his quest was in sight, for Atlas was the uncle of the

Hesperides, and certainly knew where the golden apples were kept. Hercules told him why he had come, and Atlas must have laughed when he heard that this man, giant though he was, would dare to tackle the hundred-headed dragon, which kept guard over the apples.

To Hercules, however, neither the dragon nor the unwillingness of the Hesperides was a sufficient reason for his not carrying out his master's commands, and he told Atlas so.

In the end, seeing that Hercules was determined to get possession of the apples by some means or other, Atlas made a suggestion :

" If you will hold up the heavens for a little while, I will go and bring the apples to you."

Now, you have seen that Hercules was no weakling. A man who could kill the Nemean lion, could fight the nine-headed Hydra, and tame the Cretan bull, besides doing many other doughty deeds, had to be strong ! Yet it seemed a most amazing task to hold up the skies, even for the little time that Atlas would require to go to the garden and back. I think Hercules must have been one of those men who were afraid of under-taking nothing, for he said :

" All right ! " and in a few moments Atlas was stretching his great body, and feeling the delight of freedom after years and years of bearing the burden of the skies, while Hercules was standing with legs wide apart, and holding upon his great shoulders a weight which threatened to bend him in half !

I fancy I can hear him say, " Hurry up ! " as Atlas swung out across the mountains.

When Atlas reached the garden and told the fair

maidens what he had come for, there was much weeping, and only when Atlas said that he would make Hercules promise to bring back the apples, would the Hesperides part with them.   There was no risk of Hercules breaking his word ; he was a man of honour, and the Hesperides knew that it would go ill with Eurystheus if he tried to keep the apples after Hercules had pledged himself to return them.

Hercules had grown terribly weary by the time Atlas came back ; and he was very pleased when he saw the huge giant with the three apples in his hand.   He felt that he had at last finished the great quest.

But he had not !   Atlas, rejoicing in his new-found freedom, refused to give up the apples, saying that it did not matter who took them to Eurystheus so long as the king obtained them.

Hercules was very angry.   He stamped his feet, as best he could, and the heavens shook, and the earth trembled.   It seemed that the sky would fall !   Indeed, I believe that if Hercules had not thought of a trick by which he could shift his burden back on to the shoulders of Atlas, he would have let it tumble !

What he did, however, was to agree, or pretend to agree, to Atlas's suggestion ; and poor old Atlas was so entirely deceived that when Hercules said :

" Well, before you go, you might just hold up the heavens while I put this cushion on my shoulder ? "

Atlas fell into the trap ; he laid the apples on the ground, stood up beside Hercules, and the serious and considerable task of shifting the clouds from one pair of shoulders to another was carried out without accident.

Then the hoodwinked Atlas knew that he had been

tricked. Hercules calmly picked up the golden apples, and promising to bring them back, walked away ; and despite all the callings and all the threats of Atlas, neither turned nor looked back !

And poor Atlas was left to bear his old burden, while Hercules, after a long journey, reached Argos, and handed the apples to Eurystheus, who felt that he was the luckiest of men. Hercules, however, somewhat damped his self-congratulations by telling him that the apples must be returned to the Hesperides ; and Eurystheus, who stood in such dread of his powerful servant, had to give them into his keeping, after feasting his eyes upon them for a while.

Hercules, keeping his promise to Atlas, took the golden apples, which had cost so much hard work to obtain, to Minerva, who undertook to send them to the Hesperides.

And that's how Hercules found, and returned, the three golden apples of the Hesperides.

13.—THE LAST LABOUR OF HERCULES

WHEN Eurystheus found that the eleventh labour, which he had thought likely to put an end to Hercules, had not had that result, he cudgelled his brains to discover a new task that should be harder than all the others put together. At last he thought he had it. Down in the underworld was a three-headed dog named Cerberus, and round each of his heads was a mane of writhing snakes, while his tail was a huge serpent. Moreover, Cerberus was as large as an elephant, and

The Labours of Hercules

any mortal who dared to cross the river Styx was torn to pieces by this dread guardian of the land of whispers.

Eurystheus felt that by setting Hercules the task of bringing this fearsome creature to the upper world, he would surely encompass his destruction ; and it was a fitting finish to a series of wonderful exploits most successfully accomplished.

Although he knew that this adventure was one not lightly to be entered upon, and one from which he might never return, yet Hercules, true to his terms of service, buckled on his armour, over that placed the skin of the Nemean lion, and set out, accompanied by Mercury, who was to show him the way, and Minerva, who felt that he might need her assistance on this the final task before he should have purged himself of the blood-guiltiness which his madness had brought upon him.

The passage into the underworld was at Tærnarus, a rocky point in Greece, where deep and wide clefts dropped sheer into the unknown. Hercules and his companions journeyed into the darkness of the mountain cave, went down and down until at last they came to the river Styx—the dark river across which those whose journey led them to the court of Pluto must pass in the boat of Charon, the ferryman. When Hercules arrived there, he demanded of Charon room in the boat, but the ferryman said that Hercules was so big that the boat would not carry him. There was nothing for it but to trust to the guidance of Mercury, who took him to the other side.

Once there, the adventures of Hercules began.

You will read elsewhere in this book of Medusa's

head, which turned those who looked upon it into stone, and of how Perseus, when he went to bring it, had to see its reflection in the shield of Minerva. In order to impede Hercules in his task, when he crossed the Styx there suddenly appeared before him the Medusa's head. Hercules feared this no more than he feared Orthrus, the two-headed, or Geryon, the three-headed. He raised his sword as though he would strike at the petrifying head, and the Gorgon fled before him in terror.

Pluto and Proserpine received Hercules kindly; he was a mortal whose fame had spread even to the lower world, and knowing that the gods had decreed the servitude of the hero who had never failed in any mission on which Eurystheus had sent him, Pluto, when Hercules told him why he had come to the under-world, agreed to allow him to take Cerberus to earth on condition that it was done without force of arms.

This meant that Hercules must not hurt the giant monster, whose three heads were poison-fanged, and every strand of whose mane was a writhing poisonous snake! But Hercules did not mind what restrictions were placed upon him; he had come to take the dog to the light of day, and take him he would.

So he fastened the monster with a great chain, and in spite of the bitings and snappings of the dog, which roared out with anger at being handled in such a manner, Hercules began to drag Cerberus through the shadow-land. The thunderous roll of the voices of Cerberus echoed and echoed through the cavernous depths, but Hercules took no notice of the roarings or of the snappings. He kept on with his hauling,

"In all that great multitude of fishes there was none that had the hook
in his mouth"

"Naisi lifted Deidre high upon his shoulder"

drawing nearer and nearer the upper world, until at last the full blaze of day was reached.

Cerberus, maddened by the light of the sun, struggled at the chain by which Hercules held him, and, finding that all his efforts were in vain, began to foam at the mouth, to the terror of the people of earth, who fled from the apparition which had issued from the bowels of the earth, drawn by a man clad in armour and the skin of a lion. But Hercules went on and on until he reached Argos, and the straining Cerberus dropped foam on the ground, from which there grew weeds so poisonous that everyone who ate of them died.

Imagine the feelings of the cowardly Eurystheus when Hercules turned up at court with the fearful-looking beast! I fancy the king wished that he had never sent his servant upon that last venture.

And no one on earth was more relieved when at last Hercules, having obtained a good deal of amusement out of the fear of Eurystheus, set off with Cerberus, and returned him to the place where he belonged.

That was the last labour of Hercules done at the command of Eurystheus. Henceforth he was free of the bondage in which he had been held, and he knew once again that peace of mind which had been his in the days before his madness.

But, even then, Jupiter, who had promised him immortality if he used his great strength aright, made it quite clear to Hercules that he must keep in check the fierce temper that had brought so much evil upon him. Although it does not come into our story of the twelve labours of the hero, yet we cannot better end than by saying here that, a long time after his deliverance

H

from the service of Eurystheus, and after many other
adventures, he died at the hands of his wife, Deianira,
who was misled by a sorcerer into believing that if
she only dropped on to one of her husband's garments
some blood taken from a Centaur killed by one of his
arrows, she would always be able to keep his love.

That sorcerer was only plotting the destruction of
Hercules, but poor Deianira did not know that; so
one day she sprinkled the blood upon the shirt her husband was to wear. When he had worn it some time
the heat of his body made it cling to his flesh, and the
poison burnt into him. Hercules knew that the end
had come. He built his own funeral pyre, cutting down
great trees in the forest and piling them on top of one
another. Then he mounted the pyre and told one of
his faithful attendants to set fire to it.

The wind caught the flames, which spread higher
and higher; the smoke ascended in clouds, which
wreathed about the body of the hero lying on the pyre.
Hercules suffered no pain; he had lived his life, wiping
out the stains which his madness and temper had left,
and Jupiter kept the promise he had made him; he sent
a great storm which battled about the pyre, and in the
midst of the thunder and the lightning there came a
cloud which hovered over the pyre and carried the soul
of Hercules away to Olympus, where he was changed
into a god.

A Legend of Old Japan

HI-KO was the greatest of hunters. Ho-no, his brother, was a fisherman in the days of old Japan. Ho-no, who seemed never to have any luck with his fishing, once proposed that they should change places, to which Hi-ko agreed, for he was a very generous man.

When the two men went their different ways, Ho-no was as unsuccessful in his hunting as he was in his fishing, and Hi-ko caught no fish, however much he tried.

To make matters worse, one day he lost the fish-hook. It was a sad Hi-ko who went home at night and told his brother of what had happened. Ho-no flew into a tearing rage, for until then the hook that was lost was the only one in existence. Poor Hi-ko tried to calm him by setting to work and making many new hooks—quite as good as the one that was lost—but Ho-no, when they were brought to him, refused them.

" No ! " he cried. " I will have none but the one you lost ! "

Seeing that Hi-ko had lost the hook through a big fish making off with it—that fish was the only bite he had had all day—it was no easy task that his brother had set him when he demanded that the hook be returned.

Hi-ko went down to the sea-shore, and while he was

wondering what he could do, he suddenly came face to face with a very old man.

" Well, young man," said the stranger, " what is the matter with you to make you look so sad ? "

" I've lost my brother's fish-hook," said Hi-ko. " He is very angry, and won't be satisfied unless I find it again. But how can I hope to do that ? "

" My son," said the old man, " there is no need for you to worry. I can help you to get your hook."

Hi-ko looked at him wonderingly, for how could so old a man assist him, however kind he might seem to be ?

The stranger saw the doubt on Hi-ko's face and laughingly said :

" I am the ruler of the tides, and I can show you how to go in search of that hook."

When Hi-ko heard who the man was, he felt more confident, and without asking any questions he took his seat in a magic wicker boat which the old man produced.

" Go, my son—seek the lost hook," and at the words the boat began to move, carried forward as though by some invisible paddle. The sky was tinged by the setting sun, and the sea caught the radiance of the heavens—a blaze of colour was all around him, and Hi-ko took new heart of hope.

Then suddenly something happened : the wicker boat began to sink. Now, you must understand that in the days when all this took place, the sea did not drown people as it does to-day ; men could go below the surface quite safely. So Hi-ko was not a bit nervous as, down, down into the waters where it seemed the

A Legend of Old Japan

fiery ball of the sun was plunging, he slipped. He
was quite sure that this was part of the plan the ruler of
the tides had when he sent him in quest of the hook.

Presently Hi-ko could see beneath him a view of
enchantment : on the bank of a beautiful lake stood a
palace gleaming in the light that filtered through the
water ; and coming out of the palace was a maiden
fair and lovely. She carried a crystal jar, which,
stooping, she dipped into the lake.

Hi-ko was so astonished to find such a wonderful
palace beneath the sea that he bent too far over his
little boat, lost his balance, and went tumbling through
the water.

Fortunately a tree with wide-spreading branches
growing on the shore of the lake broke his fall ; but the
noise he made startled the girl drawing water, and she
cried out. She dared not look up, but gazed wonderingly into the water where the reflection showed Hi-ko
caught in the tree. For a time she looked at it, fearful
of what this strange being might be doing there, but
at last, dropping the crystal jar, she rushed off to the
palace. Standing on the broad white steps was an old
man.

" What's the matter, my daughter ? " the old man
asked the girl.

" A son of the gods has come ! " she cried, and,
leading him to the edge of the water, showed him
poor Hi-ko clinging desperately to the branches of the
tree.

The girl and the man looked at him for some time,
and then the former said :

" If it should be that he is come from the land of

Japan, then we must receive him kindly, for he must
be divine."

Hi-ko was highly pleased to hear such talk, and
calling out to them, he told them who he was.

They invited him to leave his precarious perch, and
he succeeded in getting down without hurting himself.
Then the old man took him into the palace and gave
him a feast at which he was the guest of honour.

Hi-ko told the old man his story, and why he had
come from the land of Japan, and he was very pleased
when he learned that his benefactor was the king of the
sea, and the beautiful girl, his daughter, the Peerless
Jewel Lady.

As a matter of fact the ruler of the tides, who had
sent Hi-ko upon his travels, had done so, not merely to
help him find the fish-hook, but also because he liked
the young man, and saw in him one who would make a
good husband to the Peerless Jewel Lady.

It came about, therefore, that although Hi-ko was
very desirous of finding the fish-hook, he found plenty
of time to make love to the Peerless Jewel Lady, whom
he married after a little time.

One day Hi-ko had a talk with the king of the sea
about the fish-hook, and asked what could be done, as
Ho-no would be very angry if it were not found.

The king said he would do what he could, so he
sent messengers through the ocean commanding all
the fishes to gather together. When this was done
every fish was inspected, and Hi-ko had great hopes that
among them he would find the fish which had run off
with his hook.

But in all that great multitude of fishes there was

A Legend of Old Japan

none that had Ho-no's hook in his mouth; and poor Hi-ko was in despair. He dared not go back to his country without the hook, so he remained in the kingdom under the sea for three years, and was very happy. Sometimes he thought he ought to go back, and would have caused the fishes to be examined again, but always his wife, who wanted to stay in her home under the sea, dissuaded him. At last, however, he felt he must go home, and he made the king call another gathering of the fishes so that the hook might be sought for. The Peerless Jewel Lady now was not opposed to Hi-ko's return—and she promised that if he found the hook she would go with him.

The fishes came, all except the red fish, who sent a message saying that he was very ill.

The king of the sea inquired what was the matter with him, and one of the fishes said:

"I saw the red fish a little while ago and noticed that he had a sore mouth."

Hi-ko's heart beat excitedly—for he told himself that possibly the red fish's mouth was sore because of the hook!

It did not take him long to go to where the invalid had been seen. There he found him and in his mouth gleamed the missing hook.

Hi-ko was overjoyed. He could return safely to his own land now, and when he had taken the hook from the fish's mouth, he made great preparations for his departure. Everything was ready, the king bade him farewell, and gave him two precious jewels, which possessed wonderful power.

"They control the tides, Hi-ko," he said. "One

causes the tide to recede, the other to flow, and you will
have power in the land where you go."

Hi-ko thanked him, and said :

"My father, I return to my own land alone, to
prepare a place to which my wife may come—a place fit
for so fair a princess."

"Build her a palace beautiful," said the king, " and
roof it with cormorants' wings, and there shall the spirits
give you a son who shall be the father of emperors."

This filled Hi-ko with great joy, and, mounting the
back of a crocodile, he went up out of the kingdom
under the sea, and was soon being carried along the
surface by his strange craft.

The crocodile knew the way to Japan—knew, too,
the very spot on which to land Hi-ko, who reached the
shore, and found his brother.

Ho-no looked very black when he saw Hi-ko coming
towards him, and at once demanded the hook.

"Have you found the hook you lost ? " he cried.
" For you shall not land unless you have it with you ! "

"Brother," said Hi-ko, " I have indeed found the
hook. See, here it is," and he held it before him.

Now, Ho-no, instead of being pleased at the recovery
of his hook, was angry. The loss of the hook had only
been an excuse to pick a quarrel, for he had always been
very jealous of his brother, who, he considered, was
favoured by the spirits.

While Hi-ko stood holding out the hook, to recover
which he had exiled himself from his land, his brother
made a sudden rush at him. Hi-ko was taken altogether
by surprise, and was in great danger of being killed—
for he had no weapons with which to defend himself.

A Legend of Old Japan

Suddenly he remembered the stones which his father-in-law had given him, and just at the moment when Ho-no had flung himself upon him, he raised one of the stones and cried aloud :

" Rise, O tide ! " and a great tidal wave swept up and covered the land, carrying Ho-no away.

When he saw that the danger was past, Hi-ko held up his other jewel and cried :

" Ebb, O tide ! " and the water receded, leaving the land dry. Hi-ko then began to work hard at the building of the palace for his wife. He had told her it would be ready for her on a certain day, but the trouble with his brother had taken up so much of his time that he found he could not get the palace furnished. There was much work to be done, and the gathering of the cormorants' wings for the roof took a very long time. He knew he must have that roof finished in order to keep his word to the king of the sea.

How Hi-ko worked ! Day by day the palace grew under his hands, and the time came when he had almost finished, only a small portion of the roof remaining to be put on. Wings he had in plenty, but of time in which to work very little. For that very afternoon the Peerless Jewel Lady was due to arrive !

Frantically he worked, but quite hopelessly. Coming towards the land, riding on the back of the crocodile, was his wife, and with her, a younger woman, beautiful as the rising sun.

Sad was the heart of Hi-ko that his work was un-finished, sadder than ever was he when his son was born beneath the unfinished roof of cormorants' wings ; for the Peerless Jewel Lady, the princess he loved so fondly,

105

after the birth of her baby turned herself into a crocodile, according to the commands of her father, because Hi-ko had not kept his word, and went back into the sea, leaving the child to the care of the woman who had accompanied her. Poor Hi-ko could not follow her, for the moment she disappeared the sea, which it had been possible for him to go down into without danger before, became powerful to destroy.

And the jewels which ruled the tides lost their power. Never from that day has man had control over the sea, to say where it shall come and where it shall go to.

But the son of Hi-ko, who was named " U-ga-ya," or the " Royal Child," who was born beneath the unfinished roof of cormorants' wings, lived and grew up into a strong man, and in later years married the woman who had come with his mother from the kingdom-under-the-sea. From him descended many emperors. And, according to the old Japanese legend, he was the first man to die, after having lived for more years than he could count.

The Story of Echo and Narcissus

NARCISSUS was a beautiful youth—so beautiful that everybody who saw him loved him. But though he was so beautiful to look upon, and though everyone loved him so much, yet he, for his part, cared for nobody but himself. It almost seemed as though he had been born without a heart.

Now there lived at the same time as Narcissus a maiden called Echo. She fell in love with Narcissus ; but though she was fair to look at, yet Narcissus did not love her, and at last in despair she wandered off into the mountains and pined and pined until at length she faded away and died—all but her voice, and that remained for ever to haunt lonely and solitary places as a warning to all other maidens not to fall in love with people who could never love them.

But Venus, the goddess of love, had seen poor Echo's trouble. She was angry with Narcissus for making the maiden suffer so, and she determined to punish him for his coldness and hard-heartedness towards her. And one day, as Narcissus was bending down to drink from a clear forest pool, she made him catch sight of his own reflection in the water and fall in love with it.

He thought it was some beautiful water nymph,

and stretching out his arms he tried to catch her to him. But as soon as he touched the water the surface was ruffled and the face disappeared. Breathlessly he waited until the pool was calm again ; then cautiously bending over the water he saw once more the same beautiful face peering up at him.

All day long Narcissus stayed beside the pool. Every time he tried to clasp the beautiful maiden, as he thought, in his arms, she vanished from his sight ; but every time he waited motionless for her to come back, she reappeared and smiled at him again. And he grew more and more desperately in love, not knowing that the beautiful face was his own image, reflected in the calm mirror of the water.

All day and all night he stayed beside the pool, and all the next day and for many days after that, until at last he pined away and died of love and despair. And so poor Echo was avenged.

But the gods, who had loved Narcissus for his beauty, were sorry for him ; and when he died they changed him into a beautiful pale flower which has ever since borne his name.

In summer countries you may often find it growing beside quiet pools, gazing down at its own reflection in the water as the youth Narcissus did so very long ago. And when you are wandering in lonely places, amongst rocky clifts and mountains, if you raise your voice and call aloud, you may sometimes catch the sound of a far-off distant answer. And then you may know that it is the voice of Echo haunting the rocky mountains, still moaning for the love Narcissus could not give.

How Thor Visited the Land of the Giants

THOR was the god of thunder, and was a very great and terrible person indeed. He had a marvellous hammer which, no matter how far he threw it, would always return to his hand, and with it he killed many of the terrible giants who were the deadly enemies of the gods.

While he was in Asgard the gods had no fear, for they were sure that even if the giants came to attack them Thor with his wonderful hammer would soon put them to flight.

Thor once set out to go to the land of the giants and do battle with them before they could come to Asgard. Loki, the god of fire, went with him. They set out in Thor's chariot, which was drawn by two great goats, and the earth shook as they galloped on their way.

When darkness was coming on they came to a peasant's hut, and the two gods decided to pass the night under his roof. The peasant and his wife were glad to give them shelter, but they had no food to offer to their mighty guests, and their faces grew perplexed and dismayed. But Thor saw what was the matter.

" Do not be afraid," he said. " When the gods sup with mortals they must surely bring their own food," and, going outside, he struck his two goats with his hammer, and they fell down dead. Then he brought them in and gave their bodies to the peasant's wife.

"Here is our food, yours and mine," he said. "Prepare them for our meal; only see that you break not a single bone or evil will surely come to you."

Now, Loki, the god of fire, was often very wicked and mischievous. He thought it would be amusing to see what would happen if the peasants disobeyed Thor's command—and he persuaded Thialfi, the son of the peasant, to break one of the bones, unseen by Thor or his parents.

In the morning, when the gods arose from sleep and prepared to set out on their journey again, Thor swung his hammer over the bones and skins of his goats. In a moment the heap of bones disappeared, and there stood the two animals, alive and whole, except that one of them was lame, for Thialfi had broken the bone of its leg.

Then Thor, his eyes blazing with anger, swung around upon the peasants, his hammer uplifted in his hands, and cried out in terrible tones:

"Prepare to die, since it is thus that you repay the favour of the gods!"

Trembling with fear, the peasants sank on their knees and begged for mercy, and at last the angry god relented. He would spare their lives, he said, if they would give him Thialfi as a servant, for Thialfi could run faster than any living creature, and Thor knew that such a messenger would be very useful to him. The peasants were overjoyed at Thor's consenting to save their lives, and they were proud and glad that their son should become the great god's servant, and they willingly gave their consent. So, leaving the goats behind at the peasant's house, the little party set off for the land of the giants.

All that day they travelled, and when night fell they found themselves in the midst of a great forest, with no human habitation in sight. After searching for some time Loki found a great castle, with a large entrance hall, which was as big as all the other rooms put together. There was nobody in the castle, but they made themselves as comfortable as they could, and were soon fast asleep.

But in the middle of the night a great noise was heard, and the whole building shook as though it were in the midst of an earthquake. They were all dreadfully frightened, yet they did not dare to go out in the darkness to see what was the matter. They thought that if there were danger about it was safer for them to stay where they were. So they took refuge in a chamber with a long narrow entrance, and all night long Thor sat in the doorway with his hammer beside him, ready to do battle if any enemy came that way.

When the morning came at last, Thor stepped cautiously out of the castle to see what had disturbed them so in the night. There, on the ground, quite close to them, lay an enormous giant, snoring so loudly that the ground shook for miles around. Thor stood looking at him in astonishment. He had never seen such a huge giant before, and he thought it was no wonder that the castle had been shaken with the noise of his snoring.

As he was standing looking at the monster, the giant awoke and sat up, and, brave though he was, Thor

was afraid to use his hammer against such a mighty
fellow.

"What is your name, friend ?" he asked.

"My name is Skrymir," said the giant, "but I need
not ask your name, for I know that you are the god
Thor. Where is my glove ?" he added, looking round.
Then, stretching out his hand, he picked up the castle—
as they had thought it—in which Thor and his companions had spent the night. The great building was
nothing else than the giant's glove, and the chamber
in which they had taken refuge was the thumb of it !

The giant seemed in a friendly mood, and when
they had all eaten their breakfasts he asked if he might
journey with them. On the others agreeing, he put all
their bundles together, and, tying them tightly round
with string, slung them over his shoulders. Then they
journeyed on.

When night came again, Skrymir found a place for
them to sleep under a mighty oak. He threw the
bundle of food to them, and then lay down on the ground,
saying that he was not hungry, but that they might eat
if they would; and in a few minutes he was fast asleep
and snoring.

Thor and Loki and Thialfi were very hungry, for
they had travelled a long way since breakfast. But to
their surprise and dismay they found that not even
Thor himself was able to break the strings with which
Skrymir had tied up the bundle of food. For a long
time he struggled with the knots, then at last, in a passionate fit of anger, he seized his hammer, and rushing
at Skrymir, he flung it with great force at the sleeping
giant's head. It was a blow which would have killed

112

"Iduna laughed at him. Who had ever heard of better apples than hers?"

"He set them adrift upon the wide ocean, to be carried where the waves
willed"

any ordinary giant, but to Thor's amazement Skrymir merely opened his eyes and yawned.

" I think a leaf fell on my head and awakened me," he said. " Are not you others ever going to sleep ? "

Thor was ashamed that he—the mighty god of thunder—was not strong enough to open a bundle of food. So he said nothing, and he and Loki and Thialfi lay down under another tree, while the giant rolled over and was soon snoring again.

But Thor could not go to sleep that night. For a long time he lay listening to the noise of the giant's snoring, while his heart burnt with anger and indignation. He grew angrier and angrier, and at last he rose from the ground, and flung his hammer again at the giant's head with such tremendous force that he thought he must surely have killed him this time.

Skrymir sat up with a start.

" Why, an acorn must have fallen on my head," he cried. " How are you, Thor ? Were you disturbed too ? "

But Thor went away hastily, and flung himself down on the ground again.

He felt dreadfully ashamed to think that his blows should have so little effect upon the giant, and when at last day dawned and he saw that Skrymir was still fast asleep, he determined to make one more effort to kill him. But though the force with which he swung the hammer was greater than he had ever displayed before, yet it seemed to have no effect upon this wonderful creature. Skrymir sat up and rubbed his cheek, and said :

" I will not sleep again under an oak tree ! What with leaves and acorns and twigs falling on my face I have had no peace all night ! But now, since it is daylight let us be journeying on again. I must leave you, but you will soon reach the land of the giants, which is where you say you want to go. Only mind, when you reach the city, see that you do not make too much of yourselves, for those who live there will not stand boasting from such puny creatures as you ! If you take my advice you will turn back, but if you still wish to go forward there is the road you must take."

Then he took up his bundle and went on his way, while Thor and his companions journeyed onward to the city of the giants.

They soon came in sight of it. It was surrounded by a high wall and towers so tall that they seemed to reach up to the sky. When they came to the gate they found it locked and barred, but the bars were set so wide apart that they were able to creep through them. Then they walked on through the streets of the city until they came to a great hall, and there they found the giant king sitting with many other giants around him.

When the king saw Thor he recognised him at once.

" Surely you are the great god Thor," he said. " But I had no idea you were so small and puny ! Perhaps your strength is greater than your size ? What can you do, for no one may remain in this city who cannot in some feat excel all other people ? "

" Then try me at the feast ! " cried Loki at once. " I can eat quicker than anyone, and will undertake an eating match with anybody you like."

How Thor Visited the Land of the Giants

" Very well," said the king. " See that you make good your boastful words."

Then the giants brought in a huge trough of food, which they placed before the king; and the king called one of his men named Logi to come to compete with Loki. Loki placed himself at one end of the trough and Logi at the other, and each of them began to eat as fast as he could, until in a very short time they met in the middle of the trough. But when they had finished it was found that while Loki had eaten up all his food, yet Logi had consumed the food and the wood of the trough as well, and all the giants cried out that Loki was beaten and that Logi was the winner.

Then the giant king turned to Thialfi and asked him what he could do.

" I will run a race with anyone who may be set against me !" answered Thialfi; and the king called to a young man named Hugi to come and run against him. All the company went out to watch the match, but though the runners tried three times, yet each time Thialfi was hopelessly beaten, and at last he had to give in and own that Hugi was a better runner than he.

Then the king turned to Thor. " What feats can you perform, great Thor ? " he asked mockingly, and Thor cried out :

" I will wager that I can win a drinking match with anyone, whosoever he be ! "

" Very well," said the king, "we will see." Going back into the hall he called for his cupbearer, who came bringing a drinking-horn in his hands, which the king presented to Thor.

115

" See," said he, " whosoever is a good drinker will empty that horn at a single draught, though some men make two of it. But there is no one here who cannot empty it in three, be he ever such a weakling."

Thor took the horn. Although it was very long it did not seem to him to be of such a very great size. Throwing back his head and setting it to his lips, he began to drink as deeply as he could, in order to empty it at one draught. But when he set the horn down he found that he had scarcely made any difference in it at all.

" Never would I have believed it, if it had been told to me, that Thor could not have taken a greater draught than that ! " said the king; and Thor, without answering, seized the horn again and drank an even deeper draught than before. But when he looked again at the cup, he found that it was almost as full as ever, though now it could be carried without spilling. Then, furiously angry, he seized it again, and drank and drank and drank, until at last he was obliged to pause and take breath. But yet the cup was only a very little lower, and, full of shame, he handed the horn back to the cupbearer.

" Let me try another feat," he said to the king, and the king called to his side a huge grey cat.

" We have a game here which we play with our children," he said. " It consists merely in lifting my cat from the ground, and had you not failed in the first test I should never have dared to propose such a trifling feat to the great god Thor. But now see what you can do."

Thor advanced boldly to this new trial, but though

116

he strained and tugged with all his might, yet he could do no more than lift one of the cat's feet from the ground. The giant king laughed heartily at his vain efforts, and Thor, growing furiously angry, turned to him, saying :

" There is some enchantment here ! Let but one of your young men come and wrestle with me in fair fight and see if I will not overthrow him ! "

" There is none here who would not think it beneath him to wrestle with such a little fellow as you," said the king. " But let someone call hither my old nurse. Thor may wrestle with her if he will."

An old, old woman, bent with age, came into the hall, and at first Thor refused to wrestle with one so old and feeble. But at last, goaded by the taunts of the giants, he sprang forward, thinking to lift the old woman from the ground in a moment. But once again he found that he had met his match. Not only could he not prevail against the old woman, but in the end he himself was forced to his knees, and was obliged to own himself beaten.

Then the king rose to his feet and said that it was enough, and he called Thor and his companions to come and feast since it was growing late. He treated them well, and they passed the night there in peace, and the next day prepared to leave the giants' city.

The king made them eat a good breakfast before they departed, and went with them himself to the gate. When he said good-bye, he asked Thor whether he was pleased with the result of his journey.

" Indeed, that I am not ! " said Thor. " It seems that I have brought much shame upon myself, and I am grieved that you should think me so weak and feeble."

"Now I can tell you the truth," said the king, " since you are out of my city, which, so long as I live, I will take good care that you shall never enter again ! Had I known how strong you were, you should never have entered it this time. It was only by deceiving you that we were able to keep you from doing us terrible harm. I was the giant Skrymir; I had tied the bundle of food with iron bands so that no man in heaven or earth could loose it. When you struck those terrible blows at me with your hammer I held a mountain between me and you—though you could not see it—else had I surely been killed on the spot. You made three great clefts in the mountain with your blows, as you will see when you pass it by. And when you reached the city and entered into contests with my followers, I was again obliged to deceive you, or else no one could have stood against you for one moment. Logi was no man, he was nothing but a devouring flame, and therefore was Loki beaten at the trough. Hugi was thought—and no man, however swift he may be, can keep pace with thought. And as for you, unless I had seen with my own eyes the feats you performed, I should never have believed them possible ! For the horn you tried to empty had its end in the sea, and when you come to the sea-shore you will see what a difference you have made in it. The grey cat you tried to lift was the great sea-serpent, who lies coiled around the whole earth, and, indeed, we trembled when we saw that you had one foot off the ground for fear lest you should accomplish the deed altogether. And as for my old nurse, she was nothing else but old age, with whom no man, however strong he be, can contend. Farewell, it will be better if you come this way no more."

Thor heard him out to the end in wonder and astonishment, then, full of anger at the way he had been deceived, he raised his hammer to throw it at the giant. But in a moment the king had disappeared, and in the place where the city of the giants had been standing was nothing but a great plain.

Then the gods turned and went slowly home to Asgard, thinking of all the things that they had seen and heard. And to this very day there is a mountain in the north which bears the marks of Thor's hammer, which he made when he tried to kill the sleeping giant, and never again has the sea been as full as it used to be before Thor took that wonderful drink.

St. David and the Green Leek of Wales

ST. DAVID was a brave Welsh knight, and one of the Seven Champions of Christendom. Like all the other brave knights who lived in the days of old, he travelled in foreign lands, seeking adventures and doing noble deeds. The fame of his exploits reached his native country, and the people of Wales were proud and glad to think that they had such a champion to fight for them should it ever become necessary.

And after a time it did become very necessary. A horde of savages overran the little country of Wales, and wrought dreadful havoc amongst the people, burning their towns, trampling down their cornfields, and killing their men and women, and even their little innocent children.

The people fought bravely against the enemy, but the savages were too strong for them, and it seemed as if the little Welsh nation would be completely crushed.

At last, in their distress, the people remembered St. David, and they sent a despairing message to him, begging him to come and help them. When St. David heard of their terrible plight, his heart burned with anger, and he hastened back to Wales to succour his people.

On the way he gathered many brave knights around

St. David and the Green Leek of Wales

him to help in the coming struggle, and by the time
he reached the borders of Wales he had a goodly company riding with him. It was a little army compared
with the great hordes of savages it had come to fight,
but it was made up of some of the bravest and finest
men in the world.

When the Welsh people heard that their champion
had come to help them, their joy knew no bounds.
They flocked to meet him on his way, and all who were
able to bear arms at all joined his little army, determined, under his standard, to make one last effort to
overthrow their enemy.

It was not long before the savages heard of the arrival
of St. David. They poured down upon his knights from
the hills in which they were encamped, and then began
a dreadful battle. So fiercely did they fight, and so
closely were the two armies mixed together, that it was
impossible to distinguish friend from foe, and St.
David began to be afraid lest his knights should kill
each other in the heat and confusion of the conflict.

The fighting was going on in the midst of a great
field planted with leeks, and in his extremity a sudden
inspiration came to St. David. Bending down from his
horse he gathered one of the leeks and fastened it in
his helmet. Then, raising himself in his saddle, he cried
in a loud voice :

" Let all who fight to-day for God and Wales wear
a green leek in token of their truth and loyalty. Then
follow me—and God defend the right ! "

St. David's followers plucked the green leeks which
were growing around them, and each man fastened the
token in his helmet. Then, with shouts and cheers,

the little army charged against the enemy once more. The fight was fierce and long, but now St. David's men could recognise each other, and they were no longer in danger of being cut down by their comrades. And so bravely did they fight that at last the ranks of the enemy broke before them, and the savages fled, pursued on all sides by the victorious Welsh people.

And so Wales was saved from the invaders, and the people were able to go back to the homes from which they had been driven out. And ever afterwards, on the 1st of March, which was the day on which the great battle was fought, the Welsh people have worn a green leek in remembrance of St. David, who saved their land from destruction and their nation from the sword.

The Man in the Moon

ALONG, long time ago an old man went into a wood to cut sticks on a Sunday morning. He had been in the habit of doing this for a long time, although the people in the village where he lived had often and often begged him not to do it.

"Wait until to-morrow, it will be Monday then, and you can cut all the wood you want," they said to him, but the old man only laughed.

"Sunday on earth, or Moonday in heaven, it is all the same to me," he said.

And so on this Sunday morning, while others went to pray, he went out as usual to gather his load of wood.

When he had cut all the wood he wanted he made the faggots up into a bundle and slung it over his shoulder, then turned towards home.

The cottage where he lived was some way off, and to reach it he had to pass by the church where the rest of the villagers were singing and praying. Just outside the church he met a man, a stranger, dressed in a curious outlandish dress.

"Pray, friend," said the stranger, "how is it you are gathering sticks to-day? Do you not know it is Sunday, when no man may work?"

"Sunday on earth, or Moonday in heaven, it is all the same to me," said the old man with a rude laugh;

and he was about to pass on his way, when the stranger
stepped in front of him with uplifted hand. He seemed
to the old man to have suddenly grown taller, and his
face was very terrible to look at as he said sternly:

" Since you will not keep Sunday on earth, you shall
keep a perpetual Moonday in heaven," and suddenly
the old man found himself swept up into the air and
carried to the moon, where he was condemned to pick
up sticks for ever.

And even to this day you may see him when the
moon is full, a little wizened figure, with a bundle of
faggots over his shoulder—a perpetual warning to the
people of earth not to pick up sticks on the Sabbath
day.

The Story of Apollo

APOLLO was Jupiter's son, and he was a very great person indeed amongst the gods. His duty was to drive the chariot of the sun day by day across the sky. Every morning his handmaiden Aurora, the dawn, aroused him from sleep, and while she hastened to throw open the gates of heaven, Apollo mounted his golden chariot drawn by his fiery, high-spirited horses and drove out to begin his daily course around the world. And at the end of his day's journey, when his chariot sank down into the western sea, a golden boat was waiting for him to bear him back in safety to his palace in the east.

Once Apollo offended his great father, and Jupiter in anger banished him to earth for awhile to punish him. Apollo was very unhappy at being banished from his father's kingdom, but he had one gift which was a great consolation to him in his exile. He loved music passionately, and so beautifully did he sing and play upon his golden lyre, that there was no one in heaven or earth who could rival him.

During his banishment he entered the service of a king, named Admetus. Admetus admired Apollo's songs so much that he made him his chief shepherd, and there for a long time Apollo lived and worked, tending the sheep of King Admetus, and making his wonderful music.

So marvellous was this music that even the trees
and stones listened to it and obeyed it. Once Apollo
went to help Neptune, the sea-god, build the walls of
Troy. But he did not wish to do any of the hard
work himself, so, sitting down on the ground, he
played such a wonderful tune that the stones rolled
into their places of their own accord.

At last Apollo's punishment was ended, and returning to the sky he once again took his place as
the charioteer of the sun. After his stay on the earth
he became very gracious to the men and women who
lived there. As he drove across the sky on his daily
journey his face was ever turned down upon them,
smiling at them, and he was always ready to hear and
grant their petitions. And in return the people who
lived on the earth loved the sun-god, and welcomed
him whenever he appeared in the sky.

There was one young girl in particular who loved
and reverenced Apollo. Her name was Clytie, and
every morning she rose early and watched Apollo's
journey through the skies, from the moment when
he left his golden palace until the time when he sank
into the western sea at the close of day. She longed
for the beautiful sun-god to love her in return ; but
Apollo scarcely thought of her at all, and he never
grew to love her. Day by day Clytie watched, growing ever more and more in love with the young god,
until at last the other gods, in pity for all she suffered,
transformed her into a sunflower, so that she need
feel her grief and unhappiness no longer. But Clytie
could never quite forget her love for Apollo. Always
she turned her face towards him, following with loving

eyes his race across the sky. And to this very day when you see a sunflower growing, its face is still upturned towards the sun.

But although Apollo did not love Clytie there was one maiden whom he loved dearly, and that was Daphne, the dew, the daughter of one of the river-gods. Apollo saw her one day as she was wandering through the fields and meadows, and he fell in love with her on the spot. He began to come nearer to her, but Daphne was frightened at his approach, and began to run away.

Apollo could not bear the thought of losing sight of this beautiful maiden, and he ran after the flying figure, calling to the girl not to be afraid of him, as he would do her no harm. But Daphne would not listen. The more Apollo called the faster she ran, and at last the sun-god, growing more and more determined to win her, set to work to pursue her in good earnest.

Terrified, the girl rushed on until she reached the edge of the river where her father lived. Apollo was just behind her now, and Daphne shrieked aloud to her father to save her. Her prayer was answered. The river-god changed his frightened daughter into a laurel tree, and as Apollo caught her in his arms in triumph he found he was clasping nothing but a rough tree trunk.

Apollo grieved for a long time at the loss of the fair young girl, and ever after that the laurel was his favourite tree. And for many centuries afterwards the greatest musicians and poets and singers used to be crowned with wreaths of laurel leaves as a mark of honour, in memory of Apollo, the god of music.

The Glastonbury Thorn

JOSEPH of Arimathea, the rich man who after the Crucifixion had begged the body of Christ from Pilate and had buried it in his own new tomb, was one of the band of faithful followers who watched the ascension of their Lord after His miraculous resurrection. And after it was all over, when the apostles and disciples had gone back again, some of them to their own homes, some of them to Jerusalem to await the coming of the Holy Spirit that Christ had promised to send them, Joseph was never tired of talking of his Saviour and the wonderful things He had done. And at last the Roman soldiers, who could not bear to hear him speak in this way of the Man whom they had helped to put to death, put him into a small boat with Lazarus and Martha and Mary, his three greatest friends, and set them adrift upon the sea, hoping that they would be drowned or starved.

But these four faithful servants of Christ carried with them in their exile a precious treasure, the Holy Grail, the cup from which their Lord drank at the Last Supper. And so wonderful was the power of this sacred cup, that not only did it provide them with food and drink whilst they were on the tiny craft, but it also kept them safe in the midst of the

The Glastonbury Thorn

tempests that raged around them, and brought the boat at last to land.

Then the little company, still carrying with them the Holy Grail, went on foot across Europe. Wherever they went they told the story of Christ's birth and death and resurrection, and many of the people who heard it became converted to Christianity.

At last they came to the north coast of France, and there once again they found the sea before them. Something in their hearts told them still to go on, so again they embarked in a little boat, and again the power of the Grail bore them safely through wind and waves until they landed upon the shores of Britain.

They landed at Glastonbury, and as the people of the country came flocking round them, curious to know who these strangers were who had braved the perils of the sea in a small open boat, Joseph began to preach to them. It was Christmas Day, and he told them the story of that other Christmas Day when the Son of God was born into the world to save sinners.

But the people laughed him to scorn. They did not believe what he told them. They had their own gods whom they worshipped, and they did not wish to know of any other.

" Show us a sign if it be true," they cried; and Joseph, moved to anger at their hardness of heart, prayed to God to show them a sign. Then he took the pilgrim's staff he carried and planted it in the ground, and immediately the rod took root and began to spread. And there, before the eyes of the astonished multitude, it grew into a great thorn tree, and blossomed into flower.

Then the men who had laughed and jeered began to think that perhaps there might be something in the story which the strangers told, after all. They came humbly to Joseph and begged him to tell them more about his God, and Joseph told them gladly, and many of them became converted and left the worship of their old false gods for the worship of the true God.

Joseph of Arimathea and his followers built a hut for themselves and stayed at Glastonbury, and people flocked to them from all the country round to hear the wonderful tidings that the strangers had brought. In later times a great monastery rose on the spot where the little hut once stood, and it is said that for many hundreds of years afterwards the Glastonbury Thorn burst forth into flower on Christmas Day to prove again the truth of the story that Joseph and his disciples told.

The Coming of Arthur

MANY hundreds of years ago, when Britain was overrun by invading tribes, there lived a king named Arthur. He was king over the Britons, the native people of the country, who had been driven by the invaders into the mountains of the west.

Arthur was a great and good king, and ruled his people wisely and well. His knights loved him and looked up to him with awe and reverence, for there were strange stories told about his birth, and many people believed that he was more than a man. Indeed, some said that he was half a god.

The king who had reigned before him, named Uther, had been a great warrior and had won many battles for his people, though even he, great soldier as he was, could not drive out the invaders that were troubling his country. But though he was a great soldier, Uther was not a good man, and one of the wicked deeds he did brought great trouble upon his kingdom. Towards the end of his life he fell in love with a beautiful princess, who was married to a man named Gorlois. Uther made war upon Gorlois and killed him, and then took his wife by force to make her his queen. He had one little baby boy by his marriage, but the very day that the baby was born he himself died. And now came the trouble caused by Uther's wicked deed.

131

The people hated him because he had killed Gorlois, and his great lords had sworn that no son of Uther should ever reign over them. The poor queen, fearing that her little boy would be torn in pieces by the savage men, who were always fighting amongst themselves as to who should be king now that Uther was dead, was obliged to send the little helpless thing away secretly, lest he should be killed.

There was a very wise man in the kingdom at that time named Merlin. So wise was he that the people said he was a magician. He had been Uther's friend and counsellor, and to him the queen entrusted the care of her little son.

So the baby boy, the rightful king of Britain, was carried away by Merlin to be brought up in secret, and the country was left to the mercy of Uther's lords, who were so busy fighting one another to decide who should be king, that they had no time left to keep back the savage tribes who were always ready to invade Britain and lay it waste.

And so for many weary years the people were in great distress. They had no ruler, and the land was constantly being laid waste by the savage tribes around them, and they longed for Uther back again, for it seemed to them that a bad ruler was better than no ruler at all.

And then, just when everything seemed at its worst, Merlin came forward. He went to the bishops of the land and told them that if they called all the people of the kingdom to prayer, God would show them by a miracle who should be king. So the bishops called all the people together, and at Christmas time that year

the great cathedral was filled with earnest men, praying
that God would show some sign by which they should
know who was the rightful king.

Early on Christmas morning, when the people were
coming away from the cathedral after mass, they found
in the centre of the churchyard a large square stone,
white as marble, in the middle of which was an anvil
of steel. And stuck fast in the anvil was a splendid
sword, with an inscription written in letters of gold
round the hilt, saying :

" Whoso pulleth out this sword is rightwise king,
born of all England."

All the great men hastened to try to pull out the
sword, but none of them was able to do so. Then
Merlin brought forward a youth, slight and fair, seemingly little more than a child. Setting him in the midst
of the great lords and knights, he cried in a loud voice :

" Here is your king."

The lords and knights drew back in amazement.

" Who is this ? " they said. " This is no king of
ours ! "

But the boy went up to the anvil and laid his hand
upon the sword hilt, and pulled the sword easily out of
the stone. Then everybody knew that he was the king,
and bowing before him the bishops and the great men
hailed him as their leader.

People asked Merlin who the boy was, but Merlin
would not say outright. He answered their questions
in riddles, and as they thought he was a powerful
magician they were afraid to press him to speak. Most
people thought that the new king was Uther's son,
but others said that he had been brought to Merlin

riding on the crest of a wave, surrounded by a flame
of fire. There were a few people who pretended to think
that he was nothing but an impostor, and had no right
to be king at all, but those people could say nothing
when it was pointed out how easily he had drawn the
miraculous sword from the anvil.

And so Arthur came to his kingdom. It was a sad
and sorrowful kingdom to come to, and the young king
was no sooner crowned than he had to buckle on his
sword and armour and lead his soldiers out to fight
against his enemies. But there was something about
him, boy though he was, that made his knights and
soldiers fight more bravely than they had ever done
before, and soon Arthur succeeded where Uther and
the kings before him had failed. The savage hordes
were driven back, the country was freed from the invaders, and the king was able to live in peace for a little
while.

The knights who had fought so bravely for him
were formed by Arthur into a famous company, and
were called the Knights of the Round Table, because the
table at which they sat to eat at Arthur's court was
round. Although they were at peace, they did not
neglect their knightly pursuits. Every day they prac-
tised at jousting and tilting, and they held great tournaments to show their skill at feats of arms. And soon
they had an opportunity to show again their bravery
in battle. For a king who lived close by, King Leodogran of Cameliard, hearing of Arthur's success in freeing
his own land from the invaders, sent to him, begging
him to come and help him against his enemies. A horde
of heathen men had descended upon Cameliard, burning

The Coming of Arthur

the people's dwellings, killing women and children, and laying waste the land.

And Arthur came. He rode amongst his knights, clad just as they were, with nothing to distinguish him from them.

And when they came to Cameliard, the king's daughter, Guinevere, came to the castle walls to watch the knights ride by. She did not see Arthur, or if she saw him did not know that he was the king, but Arthur saw her, and fell in love with her. And when he had freed the land of Cameliard from the enemy, he sent and asked Leodogran to reward him by giving him his daughter's hand in marriage.

Arthur waited anxiously until at last Leodogran's answer reached him, and the answer was " Yes." Then his joy knew no bounds. He sent Lancelot, the greatest of all his knights, and the one whom he loved the best, to bring Guinevere to his court, then waited impatiently for his return.

It was April when Lancelot rode out to fetch the queen, it was May when he returned with her. The hedges were white with hawthorn blossom, the meadows were golden with buttercups and cowslips, and the song of the birds was heard throughout the land. And then one morning early, before the altar of the great cathedral, with all his knights and warriors round him, rejoicing in his joy, Arthur was married to the princess whom he loved so dearly.

So Arthur reigned at Camelot, surrounded by brave knights and fair and noble ladies, and ruled in wisdom and justice and truth. And the people grew happy and prosperous, and for a little while the land had peace.

A Legend from Russia

WHEN the three wise men set out to seek Christ at the bidding of the star, they passed through many countries and sojourned with many strange people. Sometimes they met with a cold, half-hearted welcome, but at other times they were received hospitably, and given food and wine and every comfort that they needed to refresh them after their day's journey.

One night they came to the house of a woman who welcomed them gladly. She took them in and busied herself in preparing food and beds for them. And while she worked the three wise men sat and rested, and talked amongst themselves of the great King whom they had come so far to find.

The woman's heart was always full of her household cares. It was so full that there was no room for anything else, and at first she was too busy to talk to the strangers or help to entertain them. She was giving them food and shelter—was anything more needed of her? But as she bustled about her household tasks she could not help hearing something of what the men were saying. They were talking about a wonderful Baby who had been born in a far country, and of a star that had been sent from God to guide them to the Baby's cradle. And at last the woman

136

grew so interested that she stopped in her work and sat down with her visitors, begging them to tell her more about this little Child.

Then the wise men told her all they knew—how they had studied the sayings of the prophets, and how they had learnt that God had promised to send a great King into the world to save people from their sins and to raise the dead to life; how they had heard that a star was to be the signal of His coming, and how at last they had seen a wonderful new star in the East, and had set out at once to find the King, to pay Him homage and to offer gifts to Him.

As the woman listened her eyes grew soft and shining. If this wonderful thing were true, if a king really had been born who could do all that the wise men said, what a difference it would make in her life and in the lives of all the men and women in the world! And it must be true, or these three kings, so great and rich and learned, would never have left their beautiful palaces to travel over the world in search of a little Baby.

"I wish I could send a present to the King," she said at last.

"Come with us," said the wise men. "We will seek Him together, and you shall lay your offerings with ours at His feet."

But the woman, though she longed to go, could not quite bring herself to do it.

"What will become of my house if I go with you?" she said. "I must finish my work and set everything in order first. Later on I will come and bring my gifts, but now I cannot." And as nothing

137

that the wise men said could persuade her to change her mind and go with them at once, they were at last obliged to travel on without her.

When they had gone the woman set to work and hurried over her tasks. She set everything in her house in perfect order, and then, gathering her gifts, she hastened after the wise men.

But it was too late. She had been given her opportunity, but she had not taken it, and though she searched long and earnestly she never found the Christ-Child, and so was never able to bring her gifts to the King.

And all through the ages at every Christmas time the woman who was too late to worship Christ visits every house where there is a child. Unseen by human eyes, she visits the little one's bedside and leaves a gift beside it, then silently she steals away. Year after year she comes, and never fails to leave her gifts, for she hopes that at last she may be able to atone for the neglect of that great opportunity, and that one day she will find the Christ-Child and offer her gifts to Him.

The Story of Deirdre

KING CONCHOBAR of Ulster, feasting in the house of one of his servants one day, listened to the soothsayer, Cathbad the Druid, who was crying, "Woe to Ulster!" and demanded to know the reason for it.

"Behold," cried the druid, "there is born to this house a girl who shall bring upon Ulster woe and calamity—on whose account the land shall run with blood!"

The warriors seated round the festive board jumped to their feet, while the father of the baby whose coming was thus bewailed looked with alarm as he saw their angry faces.

"Kill her!" cried the warriors one and all. Fierce, barbaric men were they, who loved Ulster so much that they would have given their all on her behalf. "Kill her, this child of woe!" they cried again. Above the tumult there sounded the thunderous voice of King Conchobar, and the men ceased their shouting and waited expectantly for the king to speak.

"Hold!" he said. "This thing you speak of shall not be! The girl of whom Cathbad the Druid tells shall live. I will take her away with me and put her out to nurse till she is old enough to become my wife!"

139

In amazement the warriors listened to the words of King Conchobar, who thus defied the forebodings; but the king had spoken, and no man could say aught.

The girl-child was given the name of Deirdre, and when Conchobar ·left the house of his servant, the baby went also. The king placed her in the care of a foster-mother and a nurse and another woman named Levarcham, who were commanded to guard her well.

In a bothy on a mountain near which no man was allowed to venture, away from every other habitation in Ulster, were the first years of Deirdre's life spent. Now and again, however, Conchobar would visit the place to look at the girl whom he had saved from death, and who he thought one day to make his wife.

Year by year the maiden grew more beautiful, till no woman in Ulster could hope to rival her; and Conchobar loved her and longed for that time when he could marry her.

But what the druid had· foreseen on the day that Deirdre was born was not to be thwarted; the soothsayer had seen down the years, and when Deirdre reached the age at which Conchobar could marry her, there took place the great event in her life.

Her foster-mother had killed a calf when a white carpet of snow lay on the ground, and the blood of the calf was sprinkled upon the snow. From the sky there swooped down a raven, black as night—and at that moment Deirdre came out of the house and saw: red, white and black. Being a woman of imagination she cried:

"No man will I marry except he have these three

colours—the colour of the snow on his skin, the colour
of the raven in his hair, and the bloom on his cheeks
as of the red blood of the calf ! "

Levarcham, who was very fond of the girl, looked
at her for a moment or two, and then said :

" Deirdre, my daughter, in the household of Conchobar there is a man who has these colours."

" His name ? " Deirdre asked quickly.

" Naisi is he called—Naisi, the son of Usnach."

Now, although Levarcham knew why the king had
placed Deirdre in seclusion, yet she had all a woman's
sympathy, and was willing to do all she could for the
girl she loved greatly.

" It shall be done," she said in answer to Deirdre's
wish that she might be allowed to see this Naisi of the
raven locks, the white skin and the ruddy cheeks.

During all those years, no man but Conchobar had
ever set eyes upon the maiden of the mountains—
and yet, although discovery meant dread punishment
for all concerned, Levarcham plotted and planned
so that Naisi could meet the fair Deirdre.

And they met—and meeting, loved each other with
a great love. Each knew that life would hold nothing
beautiful if they had not each other.

" Take me, O Naisi of the raven locks, the snow-
white skin, and the ruddy cheeks—take me hence, away
from the mountain where none comes but Conchobar,
who vows to marry me ! "

Naisi, who knew Conchobar's intentions, thought
long upon the matter. Time after time, when he went
up the mountain to see the lonely girl who lived now
only in the hope of seeing him, Naisi refused to do what

Deirdre asked, for fear of what Conchobar might do to the girl if perchance he ever caught her again.

But at last the entreaties of Deirdre and his own great love swept away all the objections of Naisi, who, one day, with his brothers Arden and Ainle and a hundred and fifty warriors bold, went up the mountain-side to the bothy where Deirdre dwelt.

The girl, who knew her lover was coming, was all ready for him. She came out of the bothy, and Naisi greeted her, and his men gave her welcome. Then, lifting the maiden upon his shoulder, Naisi stood in the circle of his warriors and vowed that she was his — for ever and ever. The warriors raised their swords and rattled their shields, and vowed to uphold Naisi and to follow him whither he went.

Because of Conchobar, who would be terribly angry when he found out that Naisi had carried away Deirdre, it was necessary to leave Ulster; and across the sea to Alba (Scotland) went Naisi and the warriors bold, entering the service of the king.

Conchobar heard of what had happened; and so great was his anger that no man dared mention the name of Deirdre and Naisi in his presence; the warrior was outlawed.

In Alba news of the fair beauty spread, and when the king heard of her he led his army to the place where Naisi and his warriors dwelt.

" Why do you come thus? " Naisi demanded.

" To look on this woman from across the sea," said the king.

When he saw Deirdre, her face beautiful as a rose, her eyes shining like stars, the king vowed by his sword

that he would have her for his wife. But Naisi scorned
the king and refused to give up Deirdre. He drew up
his warriors in battle array and fought long and hard
with the king's men. Many a battle did he fight
before he was able to leave the land and take refuge
on an island on Loch Etive, where he built himself
a stronghold, and dwelt a long time in peace and
happiness.

But, one day, there came to the ears of the warriors
as they sat feasting, a loud cry which awoke the echoes
of the hills. Every man started to his feet, wondering
what it might mean.

"That is the cry of a man of Erin!" exclaimed
Naisi.

"No man of Erin's cry is that!" said Deirdre the
beautiful, though in her heart she knew that Naisi was
right; more, she knew that the man who called was
Fergus of the court of King Conchobar.

Now, Deirdre, the night before, had dreamed that
three doves had come to the fastness on Loch Etive,
bearing each a drop of honey in its bill; but from Loch
Etive there flew back three hawks with three sips of
blood. Being a reader of dreams Deirdre knew that
her vision meant ill to the sons of Usnach, and she saw
in the coming of Fergus the fulfilment of her dream.
Therefore she kept silence, hoping that Naisi would
take no notice of the echoing cry from the sea.

But Fergus of the mighty voice called a second
time, louder than before, and again Naisi said that a
man from Erin cried.

"Nay," said Deirdre in agitation, "it is the call of
a man of Alba."

Hardly had she spoken than the echoing roar of Fergus boomed amongst the hills a third time, and Naisi would not be put off by Deirdre.

" It *is* a man of Erin ! " he cried. " Aye, it is Fergus himself ! Go, Arden, and meet him as he comes."

" Naisi," said Deirdre, as Arden walked down to the shore, " all along I knew that it was Fergus who called, but I dared not say so."

" Why ? " Naisi asked, and listened while she told him of her dream.

" What was it you read into your dream, Deirdre ? " Naisi asked.

Then Deirdre told him that she took the doves to be messengers of a false peace, while the hawks flying back with sips of blood were symbols of those messengers bearing away Naisi and his brothers.

" And woe be unto you, oh, Naisi, if you go to Erin ! "

But Fate had decreed ; and Naisi laughed at the fears of Deirdre.

Now, the coming of Fergus to Loch Etive had been in this wise : Conchobar, who had outlawed Naisi, one day decided to send and fetch him back to his house at Emain Macha, in the hope that Deirdre would come too, and that even after this lapse of time he might be able to steal her from Naisi.

Conchobar chose Fergus for his messenger, and bade him invite Naisi back to Ulster, and gave him a safe conduct for the noted warrior.

According to the conditions, the outlawed warrior could only come in peace to Erin in company with certain heroes, one of whom was Fergus ; the very presence of

144

either of these men would be taken as a symbol of
honourable treatment by Conchobar.

Fergus swept over the sea in his galley, and went
roaring aloud at Loch Etive.

Arden met him on the shore, and exchanged greetings, after which Fergus and his followers were taken
up to the stronghold of Naisi, where the warrior and
Deirdre welcomed him.

Then Fergus told Naisi why he had come, but
Deirdre, still filled with the terror of her dream, tried
to dissuade her loved one from going back to Erin ;
all in vain, however, for Naisi loved Erin and vowed
that he would go.

Fergus gave him his word to protect him, even
against the king, and Naisi and his brothers, and
Fergus and his brothers, pledged their troth to each
other on sword and shield.

Then they embarked on the galley, and a strong
wind bore them over the sea to Erin, where the heroes
landed and came to the house of Borrach. King
Conchobar had commanded Borrach that when Fergus
should arrive he must invite him to a feast. Now,
Fergus could not refuse that invitation without loss
of honour, and Conchobar knew this, for which reason
he had planned the affair, so that the sons of Usnach
should be without their pledged man whose presence
meant safety. Thus did the king act treacherously.

Fergus was wroth with Borrach.

" How can I leave the sons of Usnach ? " he cried.
" To Conchobar I have vowed to bring them to Emain
Macha on the day they set foot on Erin ! "

But Borrach refused to release him from the burden

of his invitation. Fergus, who had also promised on his honour to escort Naisi and his brothers to Emain Macha, sent with them his sons Fiallan the Fair and Buinne the Ruthless Red—although Deirdre would have preferred to wait until the feast was ended, so that Fergus could come too. For she was still afraid of the things she had seen in her vision, and thought that this breaking of the word of Fergus would bring trouble upon all.

Naisi, with his brother and Deirdre, went on, led by Fiallan and Buinne. After a time Deirdre would have had them tarry on the road, and wait for Fergus, but the brothers would not do so.

The brothers of Fergus vowed that all would be well, because Fergus had pledged his word on their behalf; but Deirdre was not to be consoled, and, being weary, later on lay down in a valley to rest, unnoticed by her friends.

When they discovered her absence, Naisi went back to fetch her; he found her lying asleep. She awoke at his approach, and in great anguish told him of a dream she had had in which she saw the sons of Usnach headless, and the sons of Fergus alive and not friends, but foes.

"Woe is upon us!" wailed the beautiful maiden; and yet, because Naisi would proceed, she went on with him until they came to a mountain near Emain Macha.

Here, once more a vision came to Deirdre, and she cried :

"Behold, Naisi, my beloved, a cloud as of blood hangs over your head. Turn aside, I pray, and go to

the house of Cuchullin that he may accompany you to
Emain Macha."

Now, Cuchullin was another of the heroes with
whom Naisi might go before the king, but Naisi would
not budge from his purpose, trusting the pledged word
of Fergus, and so the sons of Usnach and the sons of
Fergus came at last to Emain Macha.

"Know, O Naisi," cried Deirdre, "that by this
sign you shall understand the mind of Conchobar!"

"Tell us the sign, O Deirdre," said Naisi.

"If Conchobar means no evil against you," said
Deirdre, "he will invite you to the house where he and
the heroes of Ulster dwell; but if his heart is evil
against you, then will he invite you to the house of the
Red Branch—even the house where the spoils and
skulls of the foes of Ulster hang!"

For all the forebodings of Deirdre, the sons of Usnach
went boldly to the house of Conchobar and knocked at
the door.

The keeper of the door inquired who it was that
thus asked admittance, and when he knew that the sons
of Usnach and of Fergus, with the maiden Deirdre,
were outside, he went and told the king.

"Let the sons of Usnach be housed in the house of
the Red Branch," said Conchobar.

And, despite the protests of the now fearful Deirdre,
her pleadings that they should go back, Naisi went to
the place appointed.

Conchobar, overjoyed that Naisi and Deirdre had
come to Erin—because he believed that he might now
obtain the girl—called for a messenger to find out how
she fared.

" Go thou down to the house of the Red Branch and bring me back news of her beauty; if she be still as lovely as she was when Naisi bore her away, then will I take her at my sword's point; if not, then let Naisi keep her for himself ! "

Levarcham, who loved the girl, offered to be messenger, and was very pleased when Conchobar agreed to let her go, because she wanted to warn the sons of Usnach what was in the mind of Conchobar.

When she arrived, weepingly she told them, and warned them to shut tight the doors and windows against the coming of treacherous foes; and, after a while, went back to Conchobar. She told the king that never were there men so strong as the sons of Usnach, nor so skilled in war, while as for Deirdre, her beauty had faded.

Thus did Levarcham hope to frustrate the plans of Conchobar, who, however, did not altogether believe her and sent another messenger to learn the truth.

The second messenger arrived at the house of the Red Branch, and found all the doors and windows closed, except one small window. He peered through this, and saw Naisi and Deirdre playing chess. Not for long did he look, because Deirdre felt his glance upon her, and looking slyly towards the window saw the man's face, and knew that an enemy spied upon them.

Quietly she told Naisi, who, picking up one of the chessmen, threw it through the window and knocked out the eye of the onlooker.

The one-eyed messenger returned to Conchobar and told him of all that he had seen, saying :

" Never did man set eyes on so fair a woman as Deirdre ! "

The Story of Deirdre

When he heard this, Conchobar gave orders for his warriors to assemble and go to the house of the Red Branch to seize Deirdre and kill the sons of Usnach.

A great troop of soldiers thereupon surrounded the house, shouting their battle cries and flinging firebrands inside to draw the sons of Usnach out.

"Thus has Fergus betrayed us!" cried Deirdre, who now saw her dream coming true.

But Buinne vowed that even if his father had, by forsaking them, brought evil upon the sons of Usnach, he would stand by them. He sallied forth and wrought havoc amongst the soldiers of Conchobar, who, succeeding in getting a word with him, bribed him with land and privileges, to forsake the sons of Usnach.

Little did Buinne gain by that, for the land he received that very night was turned into waste land, where nothing would grow.

Inside the house of the Red Branch, Deirdre had heard the bargain made between Buinne and Conchobar, and she lifted up her voice proclaiming it. And Fiallan vowed that never would he turn traitor. Then, like his brother, he bore down upon the men of Conchobar, made three journeys round the house, and each time swept down men like corn before the sickle.

Then he went inside again, drank wine with the sons of Usnach, and, carrying a firebrand, sprang amongst the soldiers of the king and scattered them.

When Conchobar saw that Fiallan was true to his word, and could not be bribed, he called to him his son Fiacha, gave him the arrows with which he, the king, had won many a battle, and sent him to do battle with Fiallan.

So the champion of the sons of Usnach, Fiallan,

149

went forth to meet in single combat Fiacha, champion of the men of Ulster.

With sword and spear the two men fought, to the distress of Erin. The light from the firebrands fell upon the flashing swords and gleamed upon the shields ; and ever Fiallan pressed hard upon Fiacha. The ring of their swords sounded through the country, the crash of their shields clanged like a smithy's hammer on the anvil. Long did the fight last, and in the end Fiacha was borne down to the ground, and only his shield saved him from death. Heavy were the blows which Fiallan dealt upon the shield, and loud was the noise, and the waters of Erin answered in a wail of distress, which roused Conall the Victorious, who was a great friend of the sons of Usnach, and who knew that the wail of the waters told of danger to the king.

So to Emain Macha went Conall the Victorious — even to the field of combat, where he saw the heroes fighting, Fiacha scarce able to support the shield upon which the blows of Fiallan were falling. Craftily and quickly, Conall slipped up behind Fiallan and ran him through with his spear, mortally wounding him. Now, Fiallan and Conall were friends, and it was only when he had wounded Fiallan that the new-comer knew who he was. Filled with anguish, and angry with Conchobar that he should have brought such woe upon Ulster, that her own sons should fight each other, he turned upon Fiacha and slew him for vengeance.

Then, as Conall went away, Fiallan, at the point of death, called upon Naisi to guard himself, and died.

When they saw the end of the two champions, the men of Conchobar rushed upon the house of the Red

The Story of Deirdre

Branch, and cast into it firebrands; but Arden issued forth in his strength and swept through the hosts, leaving a trail of death behind him. Later, Ainle issued forth, and great was the vengeance he took upon the men of Ulster, who fled before him.

Conchobar rallied them to the fight, but Naisi leaped amongst them furiously, and the shock of his coming was like the roar of an angry wind; death dwelt in every blow he dealt, and no man of Ulster could stand against him. A brave sight was Naisi in his fury; his raven locks floated in the air, and his eyes flashed like the silver boss of his gold-bordered shield. His crimson mantle, finished with gold, matched the colour on his cheeks, and the sheen of his teeth was like that of the pearls on his silken tunic, which was also decorated with fifty ounces of bronze. Such was he who, with his gold-hilted sword and his deadly spear, hurled himself upon the men of Conchobar.

When the morning came Naisi went forth again to meet the warriors, and fought them long and hard, until alone he drove them away.

When he returned victorious, he and his brothers linked their shields together, placed Deirdre between them, and sallied forth against their foes. Before the rush of these valiant heroes the men of Ulster went down; the sons of Usnach cut a way for themselves and Deirdre through the great host, and Conchobar knew not what the end would be.

He called to him Cathbad the Druid, who, on the day that Deirdre was born, foretold the woe of Ulster. He pleaded with him to keep the sons of Usnach from getting out of Ulster, promising not to do them injury.

Cathbad cast his spells upon Naisi and his brothers ; he sent a great flood upon the land, so that they could not hasten on their way from the hosts of Conchobar, who were following them closely.

Naisi, fearing that Deirdre would be drowned in the rush of waters, lifted her high upon his shoulder, while his brothers turned their faces towards the foes. On went the sons of Usnach till the spells of Cathbad wrought evil and took away the strength of their arms.

Then Conchobar, breaking forth with Cathbad, called upon his men to fall on Naisi and his brothers and kill them ; but all refused, except a man whose father Naisi had killed in fair fight.

No strength was left to the sons of Usnach, and when they saw their foe coming they knew that the end was near.

They argued amongst themselves as to who should die first, but Naisi asked that they might all die at once by a stroke of their father's sword.

Then, laying their heads upon the block, they died as brave men, leaving the broken-hearted Deirdre, who had brought all this woe upon them unwittingly, at the mercy öf Conchobar.

True had she been to her beloved Naisi—true in life; and now she lamented his death in a dirge that swept through Ulster.

And then Deirdre laid her down and died by the side of the man who had done such mighty deeds for her sake.

Cathbad the Druid, angry at the treachery of the king, set a curse upon him; and the next day came Fergus, who, hearing of what had happened, fell upon the men of Ulster and routed them.

The Blackbird

ONCE upon a time the blackbird's feathers were not black at all. In the early days of the world his plumage was white, as pure and dazzling and brilliantly white as the untrodden snow.

One day, while flying through a wood, he saw a magpie very busy hiding something inside a hollow tree. He flew quietly up behind her, and saw, to his astonishment, that the hole in the tree was full of gold and diamonds and other precious jewels.

" Where did you get those from ? " asked the blackbird. " Tell me, that I may go and get some too ? "

The magpie was very vexed that her secret had been discovered, but she did not dare refuse to grant the blackbird's request, for fear lest, if she did, he would tell all the other birds of her hidden treasures. So she said :

" You must go down deep into the earth and offer your services to the Prince of Riches, then he will let you carry away as much treasure as your beak will hold. You will have to pass through caverns full of silver and jewels and gold, but mind that you do not touch a single thing until you have seen the prince, and he gives you permission to do so."

Then she told the blackbird how to find the underground passage which would take him into the earth,

153

and the blackbird flew off, eager to reach the wonderful treasure and obtain some for his own.

He found all as the magpie had told him. The first cavern was ablaze with silver, the second was full of precious gems and stones, but, remembering what the magpie had said, the blackbird did not touch anything, and kept steadfastly on his way. When he entered the third cavern, he found it heaped with gold. Great blocks of the precious metal were piled up round the walls, and the floor was strewn with gold dust, which glittered and sparkled and shone so that the blackbird's eyes were quite dazzled with its brilliance. He could resist the temptation no longer, and alighting on the floor of the cavern he plunged his beak into the beautiful glittering stuff.

Scarcely had he touched the treasure, than there was a roar like thunder. The cavern filled with smoke and fire, and a terrible demon appeared, who rushed upon the thief.

The blackbird managed to escape, but when he reached the upper world again, he found that his beautiful feathers, which had once been so pure and white, had been turned perfectly black by the thick smoke and flame. He tried all sorts of ways to restore them to their original purity, but he never succeeded. And except for his beak, which still retains the colour of the gold he tried to steal, he remains quite black to this very day.

And now, whenever a blackbird is startled, he flies away with piercing cries of terror, for he has never forgotten his terrible fright in the cavern; and he is always afraid of being attacked by another dreadful monster.

Lancelot and Elaine

OF all the Knights of the Round Table, brave and skilful as they were, Sir Lancelot was the bravest and the most skilful at feats of arms. Whenever King Arthur held a tournament it was always Sir Lancelot who was first in the lists. Whenever there was a difficult or dangerous quest to be accomplished, if Sir Lancelot undertook it, he was always successful. It seemed as though no man could stand against him, and his fame was so great that people began to say that it was no use for anyone to try to joust against Sir Lancelot—that knights went down before his spear at a touch, just because they knew that it was he.

Now, every year for eight years Arthur had held a great tournament, at which the prize was a splendid diamond. These diamonds came from a crown which Arthur had once found beside the skeleton of a dead king. No man knew who this king was, but the diamonds in his crown were so beautiful that people guessed that he must have been someone very great and rich. There were nine diamonds in the crown, four at each side, and one huge one set in the front, and one by one Arthur had given them away as prizes in the great yearly tournament, until now only one, the best and biggest of all, remained. Lancelot had won all the other diamonds, and now he was hoping to win the last one, too, in order that he might give them all to Queen Guinevere.

Lancelot was King Arthur's greatest friend. He loved the king dearly, and he loved the queen too. He fought for her and served her, and would have died for her, if by so doing he could have done Queen Guinevere any good. He wanted to win this last diamond for her very much, but he wanted to win it in fair and open fight. He did not want people to say that it was by his name he had conquered. So instead of going with the other knights to the place where the tournament was to be held, he stayed behind, saying that he would not strive for the diamond prize in the lists this year. He pleaded that an old wound, of which he was scarcely healed, would not let him take part in the great contest, so the king and his knights, though they wondered at the brave Lancelot letting any hurt, however grievous, keep him from the lists, left him alone at Camelot and rode out without him.

No sooner had they gone than Lancelot mounted his horse and rode after them, but by a different route, for he did not wish to be recognised by anyone. He meant to take part in the tournament, but he meant to go as an unknown knight, so that if he won he might win by his skill and strength alone, not by any favour of his great name.

The tournament was not to take place until the next day, and as the sun was now setting Lancelot determined to ride to the castle of Astolat, the grey towers of which he could see rising before him, and ask leave to spend the night there.

The castle belonged to the Lord of Astolat, an old

Lancelot and Elaine

man who in his early days had suffered great misfortunes. Since Arthur had come to the throne he had known peace and prosperity, but he seldom went abroad, and lived always in this grey old castle, with his two sons and his one fair daughter, Elaine.

An old dumb serving-man met Lancelot at the gate and went to summon his master. The Lord of Astolat welcomed the stranger and brought him into his hall, and gave him food and drink. He did not know who his visitor was, but he guessed he was some great knight, as he came from Arthur's court, and he and his two sons did all in their power to entertain him and make him comfortable.

As for Elaine—the lily maid of Astolat, as her father and brothers lovingly called her—she could not do enough for the stranger. She had never seen anyone so courtly and handsome and strong before, and she fell in love with him on that very first evening, not knowing, poor little girl, that Lancelot could never love any woman but the queen.

Lancelot was touched by the worship that shone from her eyes, and he was kind and gentle in his manner to the sweet, fair child—for she seemed to him no more than a child—little dreaming of the great, passionate love for him that was already springing up in her heart. He told them of Arthur's battles, and of the great deeds performed by the knights of the Round Table, and though he did not tell them his name, yet they half guessed that he must be Lancelot from the things he had done and the way he spoke. Then he told them that he was on his way to joust at the king's great tournament, and he asked the Lord of Astolat to lend him a shield that was blank, in order that no man might recognise him. For in his haste in setting out Lancelot had forgotten that all King Arthur's knights would know him at once by the shield he carried, and he had neglected to bring with him one which none of them would know.

The Lord of Astolat willingly promised to lend his visitor a shield, and it was arranged that one of his sons, named Lavaine, should ride with the strange knight to the tournament, and see for the first time the wonders of the king's court.

But that night Elaine, the daughter of the castle, could not sleep. All night long the face of the strange knight was before her. She felt that she could not bear to let him go away out of her life without one word more—for it had been arranged that Lancelot and Lavaine were to start very early the next morning before the rest of the household were astir. And when the dawn came she rose up from her bed, and stole down the long stairs to the courtyard, where her brother and Lancelot were waiting for their horses.

The sun was rising, and it shone upon Elaine's fair hair as she stood, half shyly, against the grey walls of the courtyard. Lancelot looked at her in amazement. It seemed to him that he had never seen so sweet a face and so fair a form, yet still he only thought of her as a child, and never guessed what longing and love for him was in her heart. And when Elaine, with beating heart, asked him to wear her favour at the tournament, he smiled gently at her and promised to do so, though he had never worn a lady's favour before and would not have done so now if he had known what it would mean to Elaine. So Elaine gave him her favour, a red sleeve broidered with pearls, and the knight took it and bound it on his helmet, saying with a smile :

" I have never yet done so much for any maiden living."

Then Lavaine brought the shield which the Lord of Astolat had promised to lend his guest. And Lancelot armed himself with it and gave his own shield to Elaine, asking her to keep it for him until he came again.

Then Lancelot and Lavaine rode away, leaving Elaine gazing after them, her heart filled with a pain that was almost a joy. For she thought that surely the strange knight must love her a little, since he consented to wear her favour in the lists. The shield which he had given into her charge she carried up to her own little bedchamber, and set it in the window where the morning sun would shine upon it and the gleam from it would awake her at the earliest sign of day. Then, fearing lest rust or dirt should hurt it, she made a silken cover for the precious thing, on which she embroidered the devices emblazoned on the shield. She spent long hours in her chamber every day, looking at her treasure, and making up stories to herself about every dint and scratch upon it. And every day she grew more and more in love with the knight, and though she did not even know his name she longed for the time when he should return from the tournament, and, as she thought, would ask her to be his wife.

Meanwhile Lancelot and Lavaine were riding towards the place where the tournament was to be held, and on the way Lancelot told his young companion who he really was. Lavaine's heart swelled with pride at being the chosen friend of so great a knight. He was full of awe and joy at the great honour done to him, and after that he scarcely spoke any more until they reached the field where the tournament was to take place.

Just as they reached it, the trumpets blew, and the knights on either side rode out to the mimic battle. Lancelot waited a little to see which side was the stronger before he entered the lists. Then he threw in his lot with the weaker, and with his visor drawn and his blank shield rode out disguised to take his part in the clash of arms. No one could stand against him —duke, earl, count, baron—all whom he smote he overthrew. Lavaine, glorying in the fray, rode by his side, acquitting himself well indeed for so young a knight.

But in the field, against the side on which Sir Lancelot fought, were many of his own kith and kin, and they were amazed and indignant that the strange knight should do, and almost overdo, the deeds of Lancelot. They thought at first that the unknown knight might be Lancelot, but then they saw Elaine's red favour in his helmet, and they said to themselves that it could not be Lancelot, for he was so devoted to the queen that he would never wear any other lady's favour. A sudden fury seized them, and jealous of their kinsman's reputation they urged their horses forward, and bore down all together upon the unknown knight. So furiously did they charge that Lancelot was overborne and thrown upon the ground,

Lancelot and Elaine

where he lay for a minute, gasping for breath and sorely
wounded by a spearhead in his side.

Now came Lavaine's chance to distinguish himself.
He burst through the horsemen that were hemming him
in, and forced his way to Lancelot's side, and with the
help of his strong young arm Lancelot managed to
climb into the saddle again. Then, in spite of his wound,
he plunged once more into the mêlée, and so valiantly
did he fight that he drove his assailants back to the
barrier, though it seemed almost a miracle to those who
were looking on.

The heralds blew their trumpets again to show that
the fight was over, and proclaimed that the prize was
his who wore the sleeve of scarlet and the pearls.

But Lancelot was too hurt to advance and receive
his prize. He turned his horse and rode half fainting
from the field, while Lavaine, seeing that he was badly
wounded, galloped after him in deep concern. Lancelot
managed to keep his seat until they were hidden in a
little wood close by, then he slid to the ground, begging
Lavaine to pull out the lance from his side.

Lavaine drew it, but a great stream of blood poured
out from the wound, and had it not been for a good
hermit who lived near, who came and helped Lavaine
to carry the wounded knight to his cell and stanched
the flow of blood, Lancelot would have died. Even
then his life was in grave danger, and week after week
he lay in the hermit's cell, tended by Lavaine and the
holy man, who knew not from day to day whether he
would live or die.

Meanwhile, King Arthur had sent in quest of the
wounded unknown knight, but nowhere could he be

found, for none of the messengers thought to search the little grove of poplar trees where the hermit had his cell. The great diamond, the prize for which so many noble knights had striven, lay unclaimed, and the king, anxious to know who the marvellous knight was, and sorry that he should have gone forth, alone and unattended, to die, sent one of his own brave knights to hunt through the wood until he should find him and carry the diamond to him. Sir Gawaine was the knight chosen for this errand, and taking the diamond he rode away.

But Arthur felt a great fear at his heart. He loved Sir Lancelot best of all his knights. Something about the strange knight reminded the king of him, and he could not help fearing that perhaps the stranger was Lancelot, and that he had ridden away to die. And when he reached home again and told the queen what had happened at the lists, and asked for his favourite knight, he found that his fears were true. Then for many a day he waited anxiously for Gawaine to return and bring him news. And Guinevere waited anxiously too, for she loved Lancelot, and knowing that it was for her he had wanted to win the diamond, she grew sick at heart lest he should have given his life for her sake.

Sir Gawaine rode far and wide in search of the strange knight, but he did not find him, for he never dreamt of searching the poplar grove. At last he came to Astolat, and stopping there to inquire he was met at the gates of the castle by Elaine, who, guessing him to be from Arthur's court, eagerly asked for news of the tournament, and begged him to tell her what had happened to the knight with the red sleeve.

Lancelot and Elaine

Gawaine, seeing that at last he had found some clue to the stranger's identity, told her how well the knight of the red sleeve had fought, how he had won the diamond, how he had ridden away wounded, and how he, Sir Gawaine, had ridden forth at the king's behest to bring him his prize.

Elaine nearly fainted when she heard that her dear knight was wounded. She did not care that he had won the prize and borne himself so well, since he was hurt, perhaps even dying. She longed to go and find him and nurse him back to health, and when Sir Gawaine, charmed with her dainty beauty, would have made love to her, she answered him petulantly, so that Sir Gawaine saw that she was in love with the unknown knight. Then the Lord of Astolat showed Gawaine the shield which the knight had left. Sir Gawaine knew it at once to be Lancelot's, and leaving the diamond with Elaine he rode away to Arthur's court, smiling to himself to think that Lancelot had fallen in love at last.

When he had gone Elaine felt that she could not bear to be left in suspense any longer, and going to her father, she begged him to let her go in search of the wounded man. The Lord of Astolat was loath to let her go, but Elaine had always been wilful, although she was so dear and sweet — perhaps he had spoiled her just a little bit—and at last he yielded to her entreaties, and let her set out in her brother's charge to search for Lancelot and Lavaine.

And after a time the brother and sister came to the poplar grove. And there they found Sir Lancelot, wasted with fever, weak and ill, and at the point of death. Elaine gave a low cry and fell on her knees beside him. Could this be the brave strong knight who had ridden away so proudly to the tournament with her favour in his helmet?

She gave the diamond to Lancelot, and told him how it had come into her care. And Lancelot smiled to see her, for he had thought that he should never look upon a woman's face again. He was not *in love* with her, for he could never be in love with any woman save the queen, but he loved her as he would have loved a dear child, and he was glad to have her beside him and feel her gentle fingers ministering to his wants. When the night came, Elaine went to the city near by, and slept with some kindred of hers who lived at Camelot. But every day she rose at dawn and slipped across the fields all wet with dew until she came to the hermit's cave in the poplar grove, where the sick knight lay. And at last by her care and tenderness she nursed Sir Lancelot back to life.

Then, when Lancelot was well again, he and his little nurse and Lavaine rode back to Astolat, where Lancelot stayed a little while to recover his full strength.

And now came a sad time for poor Elaine. She thought that the knight loved her because he had worn her favour, and she could not think why he did not tell her so and ask her to be his wife. Day by day she grew more and more unhappy, and then one morning, one dreadful morning, when she and Lancelot were together in the garden, he told her that he must go away that very day. Elaine, wild with grief, clung to him and begged him not to leave her, and told him of her love for him, and prayed him to make her his wife.

164

Lancelot and Elaine

Lancelot had never dreamt that she loved him so. He was troubled and distressed. He would not have caused her all this grief and sorrow if he could have helped it. But he could not love her in the way she wanted, and gently, tenderly, he told her so.

Elaine, overcome with grief, and bitterly ashamed that she had revealed her love, fell to the ground in a swoon. And Lancelot hastily called her attendants, who carried her back to the castle, up to her own little room, and laid her on her little white bed. Then Lancelot asked for his shield, and rode away from Astolat without seeing her again, full of sorrow at having brought such distress upon the people who had been so kind to him.

It was distress greater even than he knew, for Elaine, worn out by her grief and passion, grew weaker day by day, until at last her father and brothers knew that she was dying. Elaine knew, too, that she was not going to get better, and a few days before she died she sent for Lavaine and begged him to write a letter for her. And then she made her father promise that when she died they would lay the letter in her hand, and dressing her in her richest robes, would carry her out and lay her in a barge on the river, and send her in charge of their old dumb serving-man down in state to Camelot to meet the queen.

Her father was overcome with grief at the thought of losing his dear child. He could not bear to refuse her anything, and, wild though her request seemed, he promised to grant it and do all as she desired.

Then Elaine died, and very early in the morning they carried her out, dressed all in pure white, and laid

her in her little bed upon the barge, which was draped
in black. The coverlet of her bed was of cloth of gold,
and in one hand they put a pure white lily, and in the
other the letter was clasped close. Then the old dumb
servitor pushed off from the bank, and the barge with
its mournful burden floated down to Camelot.

That very same day Lancelot came to the palace
and asked to see Queen Guinevere. He wanted to give
her the necklace of diamonds, which he had fought for
and won at such tremendous cost. But Guinevere had
heard what all the court was saying—that Lancelot
loved the maid of Astolat, and was no longer whole-
hearted in his devotion to the queen. And she received
him coldly, and told him to take the diamonds to the
maid whom he loved.

In vain Lancelot assured her that he did not love
Elaine. In vain he tried to tell her of how he had had
to hurt the poor child when she offered him her love.
Guinevere would not listen to him, and when he again
offered the diamonds, she caught them from his hand
and flung them out of the open window into the river
which flowed beneath the castle walls.

Lancelot, grieved and hurt, leant from the window
and gazed at the water beneath which the jewels lay.
And as he gazed the barge which bore Elaine came
slowly floating by. Her face smiled as though she were
asleep. In her white robes, with her fair hair streaming
over her shoulders and the golden cloth half covering
her, she shone against the black of the barge like a star
set in a midnight sky. Lancelot recognised her, as she
lay there in her sweetness and purity, and perhaps a
thought came into his mind that he would have done

better to have given up his wild, passionate devotion to
the queen and taken the dear sweet child, who loved
him so tenderly, to be his wife.

But it was too late to think that now, for she was
dead. The knights and ladies of the court flocked down
to the water's brink where the barge had stopped, and
many were the questions that they asked. But the old
dumb serving-man could not answer them. He could
only point to the maiden and show them the letter
clasped tightly in her hand.

Then Arthur came and ordered his knights to
carry her into the hall, and they bore her reverently
in and laid her down. And everyone gathered round
her, Lancelot and the queen, and Sir Gawaine and
all the other great knights and noble dames, while
the king himself took the letter from her hand and
opened it.

It was addressed to Sir Lancelot, and said that since
he had ridden away without saying good-bye she had
come herself to take her last farewell of him. And she
prayed the queen and all the other ladies, and Lancelot
too, to pray for her.

It was a sad little letter, and tears came into the
eyes of the men and women who listened to it. Then
Lancelot told them the whole story—how he had come
first to Astolat, and had left his shield in the maiden's
keeping, and how, thinking her but a child, he had
worn her favour in the lists. Then he went on to tell
them of how she had come in search of him and nursed
him back to life, of how at last he had learnt of her
love for him, and how he had been obliged to ride away
without saying good-bye.

When he had finished, the queen came to his side and said in a low voice :

" Lancelot, forgive me ! " For she saw now that she had no cause to be jealous of his love. And Lancelot forgave her, for he himself felt that he had need to be forgiven.

Elaine was buried at Camelot with great pomp and ceremony, and the story of her tragic death was written upon her tomb. And so ends one of the saddest stories of King Arthur's court.

But it did not end the sadness, for the golden days of Camelot were nearly over, and the end of the glorious company of the Knights of the Round Table was slowly but surely drawing near.

Good King Wenceslas

ONE Christmas Day, many, many years ago, a king stood by the window of his great hall, looking out at the world that lay stretched before him.

The snow was falling, noiselessly and silently. Already it lay thick upon the ground, in some places many feet deep, for a cold north wind was blowing which had drifted it into great piles in unexpected places.

As the king watched the falling snow a man came into sight, a poor man, bent and worn, and grown old before his time with hunger and privation. He looked very hopeless and ill and unhappy as he trudged along, and his ragged clothing seemed little fitted to withstand the cold of the bitter wind.

The king's heart filled with pity as he watched the miserable peasant struggling against the wind and fighting his way through the driving snow, and turning sharply round, he called to one of his pages.

"Hither, page," he said. "Come and stand by me and tell me, if you know, who is yonder peasant, and where does he dwell?"

The page came quickly to his master's call. Everybody in the palace loved the king, and willingly obeyed his least command. For he was something better than a

169

great king, he was a good man besides, and was always kind and considerate to all his attendants, from his highest ministers down to his humblest serving-maid. His little page almost worshipped him, and he hurried to his master's side and looked through the falling snow at the man the king pointed out.

" Sire," he answered, " I do not know his name, but I know where he lives. He dwells in a wretched hovel at the foot of the mountain, on the outskirts of the forest, close to the fountain which men call the Fountain of St. Agnes."

Wenceslas—for that was the name of the king— looked after the man's vanishing figure. Then, as it disappeared from sight, he turned briskly to his page.

" Go," he ordered, " fetch food and wine and a bundle of yule-logs. You and I will brave this wintry weather and go forth to bring some small measure of Christmas cheer and Christmas warmth and happiness to this poor creature's dwelling. That surely will be a deed meet for the birthday of our Lord Christ. Wherefore hasten, page, and bring them hither."

The page hurried to do his master's bidding. He brought food and wine and packed the good things into a great hamper, and he fetched a load of faggots that would keep a poor man's fire alight for many a day. Then King Wenceslas, bearing on his own shoulder the bundle of logs, and attended only by his little page, who carried the hamper of food and wine, stepped out into the wintry blast, braving the blizzard and the bitter wind which, had they been less warmly clad, would have pierced them through and through with cold.

Good King Wenceslas

Even as it was the cold wind seemed to find a way through the folds of their thick cloaks. The snow made walking very difficult, and they were fighting against the wind every step of the way. Soon the page's heart began to fail. His hands and feet were numb with cold, and his basket seemed to grow heavier and heavier every moment. The short winter's afternoon was drawing to a close, and the gathering gloom frightened the boy, and at last he stopped short and cried out in despair to his master.

" Oh, sire," he cried, " it is growing so dark, and the wind blows colder and colder ! I am so cold and tired, I do not know how I can go farther ! "

King Wenceslas turned at the boy's despairing cry, and looked at the page with a smile that seemed to dispel the gloom of the winter's afternoon.

" Mark my footsteps, good my page," he said gently. " Tread in them, bravely and boldly, and you shall feel the winter's rage no more." And setting his face once more to the wind, the king strode on.

The boy looked on the ground to see his master's footprints, and as he looked his eyes grew wide with wonder and amazement. For a miracle had happened ! Wherever the king's foot had touched the ground the snow had melted away as though by magic, and a little narrow track of green grass, spangled with daisies and buttercups and other spring flowers, lay stretched before the page's wondering eyes.

And as the boy set his feet on that wonderful pathway and bravely lifted his burden to follow once more in the footprints of the king, he suddenly felt a glow of warmth spread over his whole body. All around the

171

snow was still falling and the wind was blowing as coldly as ever; the page could hear it shrieking and whistling as it drove the snow through the frosty air, but it had no longer any power to chill or hurt him. So long as he kept to that little green footpath he seemed to be walking through the sunny brightness of a summer's afternoon.

The little page followed his master on his errand of mercy, and the love and awe in his heart grew stronger and stronger. It was no wonder, he thought to himself, that the people called his dear lord " Good " King Wenceslas. Surely he must be a saint come down from God to show men how a Christian gentleman should live ! And the little page made up his mind that when he was grown up he would try to be just such another man as the king, brave and courtly, honest, honourable, generous, merciful and true, ready to show kindness even to a little page-boy and a poor humble peasant.

And that was how good King Wenceslas taught his page the lesson which he himself knew so thoroughly : " He who will bless others, shall himself find blessing."

The Apples of Youth

BRAGI, the god of wisdom, according to the legends of the Norsemen, had a beautiful wife, named Iduna, whose work was to guard the apples of youth. These apples were very wonderful ones, for whoever ate of them never grew old. The gods of Asgard, therefore, were very jealous of them, and Iduna had orders to see that none but the gods ate any of them.

Iduna used to sit in her garden and watch over the casket in which the apples were kept ; and only when she was sure that anyone who asked for an apple was entitled to one would she open the casket.

The great frost giants, who were always at enmity with the gods, and who had no food of youth to renew them when they grew old, were ever trying to steal the apples, but owing to the care taken of them they were unsuccessful. Iduna refused to be beguiled into allowing them to be seen by those who she did not know, and always managed to see through the disguises which the frost giants could assume.

But there came a time when one of the giants succeeded in getting all the apples of youth ! It was all through the craftiness of Red Loki the evil one. He bought freedom from captivity in the land of the giants at the price of Iduna's apples.

Famous Myths and Legends

Odin, the father of the gods, was very fond of going on long journeys, and on one of these he took with him Hoenir and Loki, and together they went clattering over the rainbow bridge which connected Asgard and earth. After they had been travelling a little time, they came to a valley in which they saw a herd of oxen. Being tired and hungry, they decided to rest awhile, and kill and cook one of the animals. While two of them caught and killed it, the other lighted a fire, and very soon the meat was upon it. The hungry gods waited and waited; they fanned the fire, they heaped on wood, and did all they could—but the meat would not cook!

When they had almost given up in despair, they heard a strange noise in the trees near them, and, looking up, saw a large eagle. Now, really, that bird was not an eagle, but Thiassi, one of the giants, who could assume the shape of an eagle when he wished.

He was enjoying his little joke—for he had bewitched the fire so that it would not cook the meat! He delighted to see the fruitless and angry efforts of the gods, and when he had had his fill of satisfaction, he cried out:

" You'll never cook that meat! "

The gods looked at the eagle in astonishment.

" What do you mean? " Odin asked angrily, and laughingly the disguised giant said:

" I'll make the fire cook it if you'll give me a share of the meat."

The bargain was made, and pretty soon the meat was cooked and ready to eat—and instantly the eagle swooped down, snatched up a leg and two shoulders of the ox!

The Apples of Youth

One would have thought that Loki the mischievous would have had some forbearance, for this was just the kind of thing he himself was always doing. Perhaps it was because he was dreadfully hungry, but anyway he was angry with the eagle for taking so much, and, catching up a large piece of wood, he brought it down with a heavy whack upon the bird's back.

But, instead of dropping the food, the eagle simply flapped his wings and began to fly; and poor Loki, to his horror, found that the stake he had hit the bird with was held fast at one end in the eagle's back, while he himself could not get free from the other!

So when the eagle flew away Loki was trailing along behind. Over rocks and stones which banged him about till he was blue with bruises, through forests whose trees scratched him badly and almost tore him to pieces —through all these Loki was dragged, pleading all the time with the eagle to release him.

It came as a shock to Loki when the bird said:

"I am no eagle, but Thiassi, the giant!" For the god knew that being captive to one of the foes of Asgard was no laughing matter.

Time after time he begged to be released, but the giant would not hear of it. For Thiassi had laid all his plans with one object: he wanted to get the apples of youth from the garden of Iduna, and he knew that of all the gods, only Loki would be likely to hand them over. When he had thoroughly secured his captive, he said:

"Loki, I'll let you go free on one condition."

"Name it," cried Loki, willing to do anything.

"You may go away if you will promise to bring me Iduna and the apples of youth!"

175

Poor Loki shook with fear as the giant spoke. It was a terrible thing asked of him ; he was to betray Iduna into the hands of Thiassi, the foe of Asgard, and hand over the apples of youth ! As a matter of fact, Loki wasn't worried over the treachery, but he knew how jealously the apples were guarded, and that to agree to Thiassi's terms would cause him to run into all sorts of danger—and then probably not be able to keep his word. Not that Loki would have cared much for that in the usual way, but Thiassi was a foe to be counted with !

So Loki argued and blustered—but all in vain. Thiassi was as stern as one of the storms he was wont to cause upon earth ; and at last Loki promised to do as he was asked.

Thiassi, with threatening words in parting, then released his prisoner ; and Loki tore off like the wind, glad to be free.

When he returned to Asgard, his thoughts were all about the conditions under which he had been set free ; and he had no idea, for some time, as to how he could induce Iduna to leave her garden.

Loki, however, was never long lost for ideas ; and, having little regard for the truth, would tell lies by the score in order to meet his own ends.

He knew that he could not hope to get Iduna out of the garden by fair means ; and he at last resorted to a carefully laid plan ; he would appeal to her vanity.

One day, when no one else but Iduna was in the garden, Red Loki stepped up to the goddess, and opened a playful conversation with her.

" Iduna," he said, " those apples of yours, which

you guard so carefully, are not nearly so beautiful as some I saw to-day."

Iduna laughed at him. For she knew Loki of old, and did not take him seriously—who had ever heard of better apples than hers ?

But Loki was not to be put off, and cried :

" Those apples you are playing with "—she was tossing them up like a juggler tosses billiard balls— " are far behind the ones I saw."

Being a clever deceiver, Loki spoke in such a way that Iduna at last began to think that perhaps, for once, he was not joking ; and anxious to know if he really were speaking the truth, said :

" Tell me, Loki, where are those apples of which you speak ? "

Loki saw at once that he had aroused her curiosity, and pressed home his advantage.

He lied again.

" Only a little way from your own garden," he said. " Just think of it ! While you imagine you have the finest apples ever seen, within a short distance are some far better ! "

" I don't believe you," cried Iduna again, indignantly.

" Well, come and compare yours with the ones I saw ! " said Loki — and waited expectantly for her answer, as on that depended the success of his plans.

For a while the goddess hesitated, but Loki jeered at her for being afraid of the comparison, until at last she consented.

Highly pleased, the tricky god watched her put the apples in the casket. She then took it up, and dropped into step beside Loki.

Iduna had fallen into the trap !

Loki led her out of the garden, and, while she was wondering whether the apples would prove better than hers, there suddenly appeared in the sky a dark form, which, swooping down, proved to be a great eagle.

Loki knew that it was Thiassi come to claim the price of freedom, but poor Iduna was terribly scared when the eagle caught her up and rose high into the air with her and the apples of youth !

Off flew the eagle-clad giant to Jotenheim, the land of the giants, where he kept her prisoner.

There was grief in Asgard when the gods discovered the loss of Iduna and of the apples which kept them young. As time went by, they felt old age creeping upon them—hair turned grey, limbs became stiff—and they had no apples of youth to renew their strength.

" Loki has done this," they said, " Loki, who is ever doing mischief ! "

So they summoned Loki before them, and threatened him with all manner of evil things if he did not bring back Iduna and her apples.

" At once must it be done," they said, " lest old age overtake us all, and render us feeble and open to the attack of the giants."

Loki, who saw what calamity he had brought upon Asgard, and realised that the punishment which the gods would mete out to him would be very terrible, knew that it was necessary to do something.

" But what can I do ? " he cried in his dilemma.

With no plan in his mind, he borrowed from Freyja her falcon plumage, donned it, and flew swiftly to the land of the giants, in the hope of being able to obtain

The Apples of Youth

news of Iduna, and, perhaps, to rescue her from Thiassi.

After a long flight he reached Jotenheim, and was fortunate enough to find Iduna alone in Thiassi's castle.

" Where is Thiassi ? " he demanded immediately.

" He has gone fishing," said Iduna, who still had with her the apples of youth, which she had refused to part with.

Loki's heart beat joyfully as he heard the news; he might be able to get Iduna and her magic fruit away !

" Quick ! " he cried, and casting a spell upon Iduna, he changed her into a nut and held her in his claws ; then, seizing the casket full of apples in his mouth, he flew away towards Asgard.

On, on, on they went—and all the time Loki was filled with a great fear that Thiassi might return and find Iduna gone ! Loki knew that that would mean a stern chase, in which the giant's great eagle wings might win.

Sure enough, before Loki and Iduna had gone far, Thiassi did return, and, filled with rage, donned his eagle plumage and set out in pursuit.

What a chase that was, to be sure ! The mighty eagle came on at a great speed, and Loki, burdened by the apples, felt his strength fast giving out.

Could he do it ?

He put forth a last great effort—if he failed now, all would be lost ! Before him showed the walls of Asgard, on whose battlements stood the gods. They had recognised the falcon plumage, and knew that Loki was coming, bringing with him the apples of youth— else, why was the giant eagle pursuing him ?

All was commotion in Asgard—all the gods busied themselves in doing something to drive off the eagle. They gathered huge stacks of wood chips and placed them all along the wall; and waited for Loki to wing his way over into Asgard.

At last he was inside—and close after him came Thiassi, who was sure of his prey. But, at the moment that he thought he had Loki, there was a roaring flash of flame; the gods had set fire to the chips on the wall, and Thiassi's wings were singed, and he fell headlong into Asgard, where he was killed by the gods.

Great was the rejoicing in Asgard over the return of the magic apples. Iduna distributed them amongst the aged gods who, eating of the fruit, were renewed in vigour—their wrinkles faded away, their grey hairs disappeared. Youth had returned.

But, away in giant land, there was much anger. The death of Thiassi had aroused the ire of his daughter, the giantess Skadi. She buckled on her armour, threw off the snow-skates which she generally wore on her hunting trips amongst the rocky mountains of Jotenheim, and with her powerful bow made haste to the vicinity of Asgard.

The gods saw her coming; the winds she brought blew cold and bitter—the clouds gathered black—the sun was obscured—and the gods knew that the terrible giantess meant to wreak vengeance for her father's death. They argued with Skadi, and offered to atone for their deed. For some time the giantess refused to be placated, but eventually she said:

"Give me a husband from amongst the gods, and we will be at peace."

The Apples of Youth

The thought of this was anything but pleasing to the gods, who, however, realised that the strength of the giants would enable them to cause untold trouble ; and they consented to the arrangement, making a stipulation of their own.

" You shall choose your husband by his feet," was the condition they laid down.

The gods were ranged in a row with only their feet showing, and Skadi inspected them. One pair attracted her attention ; so perfectly shaped were they that she thought they must certainly belong to Balder the Beautiful—a most desirable god for a husband.

Skadi made her choice—and instead of Balder found that it was Njord whom she had chosen.

Njord was the god of the sea and the winds, and always dwelt near the sea, while Skadi loved her mountains. But, having accepted the terms, and having made her choice, there was nothing to do but to abide by it.

And, as you will understand, the gods were glad that worse had not befallen as the result of the loss and recovery of the apples of youth.

The Story of Finn

OF all the great heroes who lived in Ireland far back in the dim ages, there was none greater than Finn, king and ruler over the Fianna, the race of beings — half men, half gods — about whose doings the Irish people still tell such wonderful tales.

When Finn was born his father had just been killed in battle by the enemies of his race, and his mother did not dare to keep her little baby with her, for the country was overrun by the conquerors. So Finn was taken away by some faithful women and hidden in the midst of the deep woods to be brought up safe from his father's enemies.

In the woods he grew up, straight and strong and fair-haired and beautiful, and there were none that could beat him at swimming or hunting or running. And when he was grown to be a tall fair youth, the women who had tended him so faithfully sent him out into the world to seek his fortune.

He went first to a king's court and took service with him to learn all that there was to know about fighting and bearing arms. And then he went to a great poet and learnt to make beautiful songs. He learnt the song of the blackbird and the calling of the cuckoo, the speech of the corncrake, the voices

182

of the waterfall and the rushing river, and the whisper of the reeds down in the trembling bogs. And when he had learnt all that the poet and the woods and the downs had to teach him he went to a gathering of the high king of Ireland at Teamhair.

There was a great feast going on in the king's house when he came there, and Finn, who was still no more than a young lad, came in and took his place amongst the chiefs. Everybody looked at him, but no one knew who he was. Then the king called to the strange youth, and Finn rose up and went to him, and the king asked him who he was.

"I am Finn, the son of Cumhal," he said, "the man who used to be king over the Fianna; and I am come to you to get your friendship."

"That will I give you, boy," said the king, "for you are the son of a man whom I trusted."

Then Finn sat down in the seat of honour beside the king, and the feast went on with drinking and song and happiness and laughter.

Now every year, at the high king's feast, for nine years past, there had come a strange man to Teamhair and burned down the king's hall. Every year the king had set strong men to guard the hall, but the stranger always came playing strange sweet music, so that all who heard it were laid under a spell and fell asleep. None could keep awake, though the king had promised great rewards to the man who should guard Teamhair till the morning and prevent its being burned down.

When Finn heard of the strange man and of the reward the king offered, he rose up eagerly and asked

183

if he might be allowed to keep watch that night. The king gladly gave him permission, and he promised to give him whatever he might ask if he should succeed in overcoming the stranger and keep Teamhair safe till the morning.

Then Finn went out and took up his watch, and as he waited a man came to him, bearing in his hand a long spear.

"Boy," he said, "I was a friend of your father, and I bring you this magic spear which I have kept in safety for your coming. When you hear the music of the stranger, do you place the head of the spear against your forehead, and the power of the spear will not let sleep come upon you. Only, in return for this service, I ask you to grant me one thing. When you come to your kingdom, give me a third of whatever your right hand wins."

"That will I do gladly," said Finn, "for your friendship and the friendship you gave my father." And then he took the magic spear and set himself to watch again.

It was not very long before he heard strange, sweet sounds in the distance, and he knew that it was the music made by the mysterious harper. And he laid the head of the spear against his forehead as the man had told him, and waited for the stranger to appear. The music came nearer and nearer, and all the king's men who watched with Finn fell asleep as they always did, and the harper sent a great flame of fire out of his mouth to burn down the hall of Teamhair. But Finn was not asleep. The power of the spear had kept him awake when other men fell under the spell of the music, and seizing his cloak he flung it upon the flames, and the flames went out and died on the ground.

When the harper saw that the power of his spell was gone, he gave a great cry and turned to flee. But Finn cast the spear at him, and it went through his heart, and he fell to the ground and died, and never troubled the men of Teamhair again.

At the breaking of the day the king and all his men came out to where Finn was, and they saw the halls of Teamhair still standing and the dead man with his pipe and harp lying on the ground. Then the king said :

" Well have you fulfilled your task, O Finn ! What is it that you will have of me ? "

" Give me my father's kingdom, and the leadership over the sons of the Fianna, which is mine by right," said Finn ; and the king and all the chiefs of Ireland agreed that Finn should be given his father's kingdom.

So Finn became ruler over the Fianna, and he ruled them to the end. He was a great man and a great poet, and a great hunter and a great fighter, and many were the battles that he fought and the mighty deeds that he did. He was just and generous, and he never broke his word, and his people all loved him, and followed him wherever he led.

For many years Finn lived and ruled, but at last the end came to his reign as the end comes to all things. No one knew how or where he died ; indeed, some say that he never died at all, but is alive in some place yet. And the Irish people still tell the story of a smith who found one day a cave with a door to it, and a keyhole in the door. The smith made a key to fit the keyhole, and when he had opened the door he saw a great, lofty cavern, and on the floor there were lying great strong men, with one in the middle who was greater and stronger than all the others.

Beside the man in the middle lay a great horn, and when the smith saw that he knew that it was Finn and his men who lay there in the cavern.

He took hold of the horn and raised it to his lips, though it was so heavy that he could hardly lift it, and he blew a blast on it so great that the sound he made seemed to go right through the world. And the men on the ground shook from head to foot. Then he blew another blast, and this time the men turned and rose on their elbows.

When the smith saw that, a great fear came upon him, and he flung down the horn and rushed from the cave and locked the door, and threw the key he had made into a deep lake. And the cave has never been found again since that day.

But the peasants of Ireland believe that the day will come when Finn's horn will be sounded three times. Then Finn and his mighty men will rise up, as strong and well as ever they were, to lead the Irish people to victory as they did in the days long ago.

The Great God Pan

PAN was the god who ruled over the woods. He was a curious-looking person. He had the body of a man, but his legs were the legs of a goat, and on his head he had a pair of goat's horns. He was very fond of music, and he loved dancing, and he lived a happy, careless life amongst the woods and glens.

One day, as he was wandering in the forest, he caught sight of one of the wood nymphs—a beautiful young girl named Syrinx. Pan fell in love with her on the spot, but Syrinx was terrified at his strange appearance, and fled from him whenever she saw him. For some days Pan tried in vain to speak to her, and one day his longing grew so great that when, as usual, Syrinx ran away at the sight of him, he ran after her.

Syrinx heard him following, and, more frightened than ever, she rushed on faster still. But she could not run as fast as Pan could. He was gradually overtaking her, when all of a sudden she found her way blocked by a stream.

She raised her hands in despair. " Help me ! Help me ! " she cried to the gods, and the gods sent help to her. Just as Pan came crashing through the bushes behind she was drawn down into the water, and the next moment a clump of reeds sprang up in the stream in the place where she had vanished.

Poor Pan was dreadfully unhappy when he saw that Syrinx had gone. He knew that he should never see her again, and he gave a deep sigh of regret and sorrow. His breath passed through the reeds of the river, and made such a sweet sound that Pan was startled by the sudden music. A moment he stood listening; then, sitting down on the river's brink, he gathered a handful of reeds and bound them together to make a pipe, upon which he played so beautifully that he held everybody spellbound who heard him.

He called the instrument which he had made "Syrinx," after the maiden he had loved; and often, after that, strange sweet sounds of music were heard in the forest. And so wonderful was the music he made with his magic pipes, that when they heard it the flowers that before were drooped and dying revived, and swung to and fro in the breeze with pleasure and delight. The birds hushed their songs, butterflies and dragon-flies hovered around the player; even the very sunbeams stayed still to listen to the strange sweet notes.

Even to this very day, travellers in wild woodland countries sometimes think they hear dim sounds of distant music. And they say it is the great god Pan, playing upon the pipes that he made that day by the river when he lost the maiden he loved.

The Story of Perseus

ACRISIUS, King of Argos, had a beautiful daughter named Danaë, of whom he was very fond, yet at the same time he feared greatly. An oracle had said that although he now reigned over the land, out of which he had driven the rightful Prince, Proteus, the day would come when his own daughter's son should kill him. For this reason Acrisius was afraid and always unhappy. He determined to prevent his daughter from being married, and kept her a prisoner in a brass-lined tower of great strength.

But the prophecy was in the hands of the gods, who took pity on Danaë and sent her a little son. When her father learned this he was angry, because he saw in it the doom he feared.

He had his daughter brought out of the brazen tower, vowing that he would punish her. But how to do so was the question that worried him. At last he solved it. He commanded his soldiers to take Danaë and her child down to the seashore, place them in an empty chest, and set them adrift on the wide ocean, to be carried where the waves willed.

The weeping Danaë found herself very soon far out at sea. On her bosom rested the little baby, who, because he was so beautiful, she named Perseus.

Big waves rose all around the frail craft, threatening to swamp it; the wind bowled it along at a great rate, and the scared princess, fearing for the life of the child she loved, prayed to the gods to take care of them both.

And Jupiter, who had sent her Perseus, heard the prayer; the oarless craft, seemingly without guidance, was piloted safely by Jupiter to the island of Seriphus.

On the shore of the island Danaë saw a man fishing; he carried a net and a trident, and he was looking in amazement at the strange boat coming towards him. When it was near enough he flung his net, and it fell over the chest. A few moments later he had drawn it on to the beach. Imagine his astonishment when he saw what it held!

"Have pity on me and my child!" cried Danaë, not at all sure of the kind of welcome she might receive at the hands of the stranger.

"Fear not, my daughter," said the fisherman, who was Dictys, and brother to Polydectes, King of Seriphus. "I will take you to my house, and you shall be as my own daughter."

So it came about that Danaë and her son lived many years in peace on the island; Perseus grew up, manly and strong, loved of men and the gods.

But the time came when trouble brewed. King Polydectes lost his wife, and so beautiful was Danaë, that he determined to marry her. Danaë, however, refused, and the king was very angry.

"If you will not be my wife," he said, "you shall be my slave!"

The Story of Perseus

When Perseus returned from a journey he found his mother working as a slave in the palace of the king.

Perseus went to the king in a rage, and, but that Dictys prevailed upon him, he would have killed Polydectes. So frightened was the king that he allowed Perseus to take his mother away.

"Come," said the boy, who loved Danaë as few children love their mothers. "Come to the temple of Minerva, where not even Polydectes dare try to lay hands upon you."

When the king heard where Perseus had taken the princess, he knew that while the boy remained in the island it would be impossible to obtain possession of Danaë. Therefore he plotted to get him out of the kingdom. To this end he gave a feast to which he invited many people, and every guest was expected to bring a rich present. He knew that Perseus, being poor, could not afford a present, and he hoped that the sneering of the rich men, when they saw how Perseus came empty-handed, would make the young man go off in a rage and leave the island.

Polydectes was right. So angry was Perseus at his reception that, standing before the king, he cried :

"These men bring you gifts of many kinds, but I, who am poor, will bring you such a gift as no man ever had before ! "

The king laughed in his face.

"What would you bring ? " he demanded.

"I will fetch for you the Medusa's head ! "

When they heard the boy say this, Polydectes and his guests laughed scoffingly, for they thought that any man who would attempt to get near to the Gorgons

191

would probably lose his life in the attempt. They imagined that only his anger had prompted Perseus to make his boast, and that he did not mean it.

The king, however, saw in it an opportunity to be rid of Perseus, and cried :

" I keep you to your word. I forbid you to appear on this island again without the gift you boasted you would bring ! "

Perseus, although he left the court with a brave bearing, was a little afraid now calmer thoughts were in his head.

" What have I promised to do ? " he muttered, for he knew how dangerous a task he had undertaken. Medusa was one of the three Gorgons, the others being Stheno and Euryale. The latter two were immortal, but Medusa was not. They lived in the land of night, and Medusa, who was very beautiful, and had wonderful hair, had quarrelled with the goddess Minerva, who out of spite changed Medusa's hair to writhing serpents and cast a spell upon her, saying :

" He who looks upon your face shall be turned to stone ! "

Perseus, who knew all about these things, wondered how he would manage to do as he had boasted and yet escape the writhing serpents round the Gorgon's head. While he was worrying about this there came to him Minerva and Mercury.

Minerva told him that she knew of his troubles, and would help him if he were still bent on carrying out the task. Perseus assured her that he was, and the goddess gave him instructions as to how to find the Gorgon.

The Story of Perseus

" First of all," she said, " you must go to the three Grey Sisters, who will tell you the way to the Garden of the Hesperides, who are the only ones who can help you to find the Gorgons."

Perseus thanked Minerva, but asked how he could reach the Grey Sisters.

" Here," said Mercury, taking off his winged sandals, which enabled him to fly very quickly, " take these." And he fastened them on to Perseus's feet. Then, being thus equipped, Perseus prepared to go, but Minerva called him back, and handing him her shield, which shone like glass, said :

" Take heed, Perseus, lest you look upon the beautiful face of Medusa ; to do so is to turn into stone. Keep this shield, and if you would see her, look at the reflection in that. Then shall you be safe ! "

Grateful to the gods, Perseus set out on his journey, flying through the air towards the north, where the three Grey Sisters dwelt. He found them sitting in the snow, singing a weird song ; but although he asked them to tell him the way, they refused again and again. At last Perseus grew desperate. The three Grey Sisters had only one eye and one tooth between them, and as they sang they threw their one eye from one to another. Perseus suddenly sprang in between the sisters and caught the eye !

Then was there much wailing by the Grey Sisters. One eye only—and that taken from them ! They looked well after their one tooth, lest the thief should take that too !

Perseus, now that he had their eye, thought that he could bring them to terms.

N   193

"Tell me the way," he cried, "or I will throw your eye into the sea!"

And the Sisters, making him promise to give it back to them if they told, did as he wanted them to.

"Southward must you go until you come to Atlas," they said. "For you have come right away from the Garden of the Hesperides, who alone can show you the way to Medusa."

Perseus was nothing loath to leave the land of night and cold and go southward to warmer climes. The sandals of flight carried him swiftly away until he came to Atlas, on whose slopes was the Garden of the Hesperides, where the golden fruit grew, guarded by a dragon which never slept.

Perseus winged his way into the garden, and stood before the maidens, who ceased their dancing and asked why he had come.

"To ask the way to the land of the Gorgons," Perseus replied.

The Hesperides looked at him in wonder, for he must needs be a brave man who would dare think of seeking the Gorgons. They argued with him, but when they found that he was determined to keep on the search they sent him up the mountain to their uncle Atlas to ask what should be done.

Looking out across the world, Atlas, who bore the weight of the heavens upon his shoulders, could see the Gorgons.

"Perseus," he said, "no man can go there and come back except he wear the cap of darkness, which makes him invisible."

"Then will I have the cap!" cried Perseus.

The Story of Perseus

" My son," said Atlas, " the cap of darkness is in the underworld, and how can you get it ? "

" Somehow must I have it," was all that Perseus said.

" One of my nieces shall fetch it for you," said Atlas, " if you will promise me one thing."

" Name what you will," cried Perseus, " and I will do it ! "

" Promise me that when you get the Gorgon's head you will bring it to me that I may look upon it. Old I am, and weary, and my burden gets too heavy. One look at Medusa's head, and I shall be turned to stone."

" I promise," said Perseus, and in a little while one of the Hesperides had fetched from the underworld the cap of darkness, which she placed upon his head.

Then away once more, whither Atlas had directed ; northward again, to the land of snow and night. White mists hung over the land, and all was still and quiet —so quiet, that when, later on, Perseus heard the rustling of the wings of the Gorgons, it sounded like the voice of a mighty wind.

Swiftly, and safely hidden by the cap of darkness, Perseus, looking into the brightly burnished shield, sought until he found the place where lay the beautiful but cruel Medusa. Then, mindful that he must not look upon her face, he held his shield high above his head, so that it reflected everything below ; and keeping his eyes upon it, swooped down all unseen. Then, with his sword, he cut off Medusa's head, which he put into a pouch given to him by the Hesperides.

Then up and up he went, holding the head behind
him, lest by any chance he should see it. As he arose
Medusa's two sisters, screaming in anger, flew after
him. As he still wore the magic cap they could not
see him, but they followed the trail of blood, and
had not the sandals of swiftness now come to his aid,
Perseus would have been overtaken. As it was, the
Gorgons were left far behind.

The first thought of Perseus was to keep his
promise to Atlas; he went to him, opened his
pouch, and showed him the fair face crowned with
serpents.

One look, and the great holder-up of the sky was
turned into rock—huge mountains which stand to-day,
snow-capped, their summits reaching beyond the clouds.

Then, bidding farewell to the Hesperides, Perseus
winged his way towards the east, and came at last
to the seashore. And there he saw a maiden, chained
to a rock well out at sea.

Wonderingly, Perseus flew towards her, and, coming
nearer, found her to be a beautiful princess, whose
long, flowing hair was her only clothing. The waves
and the rising tide swept round her, and her frightened
face made Perseus hasten to her, more especially as,
coming nearer and nearer, he saw the winding form
of a great dragon approaching her.

Perseus swooped down, and the people thronging
the shore heard the howls of the serpent, the clash
of a sword upon its scales, saw the lashing tail churn
the water into foam, and knew that some stranger
hero had come to save the unfortunate princess. The
fight between the dragon and Perseus lasted for a

The Story of Perseus

long time, and the shackled maiden looked on with straining eyes, seeking to discover who it was that fought so valiantly to save her from the beast which had come up to devour her.

At last the gallant Perseus won—the dragon, fighting to the end, lay dead in the reddened sea, turned to stone ! For Perseus, realising that he stood little chance of overcoming the monster by ordinary means, had suddenly opened the magic pouch, and held Medusa's head before the eyes of the dragon. The crowd on shore ran down to the rock. Here they saw the sandalled Perseus, who had taken off his magic cap, and they marvelled at this man who had overcome the dragon.

He was standing talking to the maiden, whom he had released from the chains.

" How comes it, sweet maiden," he asked, " that you were in such sore straits ? "

" Fair youth," said the maiden, her eyes alight with gratitude, " I thank you that you saved me from the doom which the wicked queen of the sea had fashioned for me."

Then Andromeda told him that she was the daughter of Cassiopeia, who was proud of her beautiful daughter, and had offended the queen of the sea by saying that Andromeda was fairer than she. Angry, the queen caused her brother, the king of fire, to send earthquakes and fires from the centre of the earth, rending the country, while she herself caused great floods to sweep all over the land. The land became barren, people starved because of the barrenness, and, to make matters worse, the queen of the sea sent the great dragon to prey upon the land. The people sought to get the curse removed, but the oracle said that only by the death of Andromeda could the sin of Cassiopeia be atoned for.

Resolved to be rid of the monster by any means whatever, the people took Andromeda and chained her to the rock in the sea, from which Perseus had released her.

" And now, fair youth," she cried, " the curse of the queen of the sea will be upon you ! "

Perseus laughed, for he knew that Minerva and Jupiter were his friends, and were stronger than the wicked queen ; he told her to be of good cheer, took her to her home, and later on, after the gods had set free the land from the curse of fire and flood, he married her.

To the wedding feast there came one Phineus, who desired Andromeda for himself. With many men he was going to carry the princess away, and might have done so had not Perseus suddenly cried out to his own friends :

" Get you behind me all ! " And when they were safe behind him he produced Medusa's head, held it before his face, and immediately Phineus was turned to stone.

Having settled that little trouble, Perseus went on with the feast, and afterwards lived in the country for some time before he returned to Seriphus. Here he learned that Polydectes had ill-treated Danaë, and he resolved to punish him.

Going up boldly to the palace, Perseus stood before the king. Then, while the courtiers looked on, and

The Story of Perseus

Polydectes, with a sneer on his lips and with a taunt ready to his tongue, laughed at the man he had sent away on so dreadful an errand, Perseus pulled Medusa's head out of the bag. Holding it before the king he cried :

" Behold, O king, the promised gift ! "

And instantly Polydectes and his followers were turned to stone.

Then, calling all the people of Seriphus together, Perseus told them what he had done, and at the same time made Dictys king of the land. After that, feeling the desire to see once more his native land, Perseus, taking Danaë and Andromeda, went to Argos. He had, meanwhile, given back to Minerva the shield which had proved so useful to him in his conflicts, and made her a present of Medusa's head. This Minerva had set in the centre of the shield.

Through all the time that had elapsed since Acrisius had sent Danaë and her son adrift in the chest, the king had been living in dread of the doom pronounced by the oracle. Never was he sure of what might happen ; some day, perhaps, Danaë and her son Perseus might return to Argos, and then Acrisius dared not think of the future. And he had more than enough to think about in the present, for an enemy had exiled Acrisius and mounted the throne. It was at this time that Perseus returned to the land of Argos, heard the misfortune of his grandfather, and fought and conquered the usurper, and then reigned in his stead.

Acrisius, who was in a far-away land, heard of all the things that had happened in Argos, and was filled

with a great dread lest Perseus should come and seek
him, in order to take vengeance for the ill-treatment
of his mother.

But Perseus was not thinking of any such thing,
and after a time, when Danaë, who longed to see her
father, asked him to fetch Acrisius, he went across the
sea with that intention.

When Perseus arrived at the court he found that
the games were in progress, King Acrisius sitting and
watching the young men displaying their prowess.
Being strong and famed for his skill, Perseus took part
in the games and carried off many of the crowns awarded
to the victors. Acrisius, watching his grandson, must
have thought of the words of the oracle, and have
wondered whether they would come true.

Perhaps rather he wondered *when*, for he knew
that what the oracle had said must happen. Anxious
though he was to take the king back to Argos, where
Danaë awaited him, yet Perseus could not fight against
fate. While he was throwing quoits, one of them struck
his grandfather's foot, and injured him so severely that
he died.

Thus, to Perseus's great grief, was the prophecy
fulfilled.

A Legend of the Milky Way

SHOKUJO, the spinning maiden, lived on the bank of the wonderful River of Silver, the Milky Way, and being very homely and industrious, spent most of her time in spinning and weaving. She rarely played with the other girls, and her father, the sun-king, grew alarmed about her; for even in star-land the old proverb holds true about all work and no play being harmful to children. But, although he did all he could to encourage her to take part in the revels of the other star-children on the great Silver River, and tried to wean her from the labours to which she set herself day after day, he could not do so; Shokujo worked and worked at her spinning.

Then her father had a happy idea.

"If she gets married," he said, "she will surely find other interests."

So, without Shokujo knowing anything about it, her father began to look around for the man who would make her the best husband. The sun-king finally came to the conclusion that Kingin, the herd-boy, who kept cows on the bank of the Silver River, would be the best match for his daughter. All arrangements were made and the wedding in due time took place, amidst much rejoicing on the Silver River.

The sun-king told himself that he had solved the

problem of Shokujo, as, indeed, he had—only to make a greater one! For where before she had been so industrious, with no desire for pleasure, now that she was the wife of Kingin, her whole nature changed. She grew idle, careless of work, her spinning lost its old charm for her, and she turned to pleasure in just the same way as before she had turned to work. Everybody had expected that at least she would be a good housewife, but she was not; and the sun-king was very angry. Poor Kingin got all the blame for his wife's behaviour, although he was not a bit less desirous than was her father of seeing her diligent. Kingin really did love his beautiful young wife, and when the sun-king came over one day and said:

"Kingin, I'm going to put a stop to all this!" the herd-boy was highly pleased, only to have his dream shattered when his father-in-law said, "I'm going to send you away from Shokujo!"

Kingin argued with the sun-king, but it was no use.

"You will be sent to the other side of the river," said his father-in-law. "Shokujo will stay here."

"Are we never to see each other again?" Kingin asked; and poor Shokujo looked so utterly miserable at the thought of losing the husband she loved that it is a wonder her father did not repent. But once he had made up his mind, nothing would make him change it.

"Oh, yes," he said; "you shall see each other sometimes. On the seventh night of the seventh month of each year you shall meet together—if it does not rain."

A Legend of the Milky Way

Imagine the grief of Shokujo and Kingin! To think that they were to be separated by the wide shining river, and only to meet once a year! They wept, they implored; but the sun-king was determined, and that evening he called together thousands and thousands of magpies, and told them to form a bridge across the Silver River.

The myriads of birds, chattering amongst themselves, flew off and swooped across the river in a long, billowing line until there was a wide, dark bridge stretched from side to side. Shokujo and Kingin stood hand in hand while the birds made the bridge, and when it was done the husband bade farewell to his weeping, broken-hearted wife, drove his oxen on to the bridge, and wended his way slowly across to the other side of the shining river.

It was morning when he arrived there, and he could not see his wife far over on the other bank; but the next night, when the stars hung like twinkling lamps in the sea of the heavens, Kingin left his herd awhile, and standing on the bank, gazed out across the river towards the spot where he knew his wife would be standing, looking for him. Night after night these two lovers would do this, waiting for the seventh night of the seventh month to come round, when they might be able to meet again. By day Kingin tended his herd, and Shokujo bent over her shuttle and loom, for the sun-king was very glad to find that his cure was effective, and the lazy, pleasure-loving daughter had once again become a diligent woman. Her father was not so anxious to change her now as he had been before.

203

How anxiously did Kingin and Shokujo wait during that long year for the night of meeting to come round! And how they trembled lest it should rain! For, if it did rain, then the magpie bridge would be washed away, and Shokujo would not be able to cross the shining river.

That first year of Kingin's exile came to an end at last; the seventh night of the seventh month was come, the magpie bridge was there, the rain held up, and, trembling for very joy, poor little Shokujo tripped across to the bank where Kingin stood waiting for her.

Not long, however, did they have to talk to each other; and when Shokujo went back to her place, the two lovers knew that yet another year must stretch between them. Year after year, except when the rain came and the bridge was broken, did the spinning-maid and the herd-boy thus meet on the bank of the shining river, and the women and girls of Japan wait none the less anxiously than they for the seventh night of the seventh month. For it is then, when the spinning-maid meets the herd-boy, that the girls wish —one night a year—for skill in needlework, or for wisdom, or wealth.

The Curse of Andvari's Gold

ODIN, the god of the old Norse people, often wandered in the world, for he wished to see how the men and women who lived there prospered. Many a time he helped them when they were in trouble, and the people soon grew to look for, and welcome, the coming of the one-eyed stranger in the blue cloak, which he always wore on his travels, for they recognised and reverenced the great god. But once when he was journeying in this way, Odin brought with him misfortune and not a blessing, a misfortune that was to last for many long years.

Odin and Loki and another god were walking by the side of a river when they saw an otter on the bank. Loki, who was always ready for mischief, picked up a great stone and hurled it at him, and so true was his aim that it hit the otter on the head and killed him instantly. But this otter was really a son of Hreidmar, the king of the dwarfs, who only changed himself into an otter in the daytime in order that he might catch fish, for he was a great fisher. And when Hreidmar knew that his son was dead he was furiously angry. He called his servants, who fell upon the gods and bound them so securely, that, powerful though they were, they were unable to free themselves.

When Odin saw that they were prisoners he spoke
to the dwarf king and told him that they would pay
any ransom he liked if he would only let them go.
And Hreidmar, spreading the skin of the otter on
the floor, said :

" If you would be free you must cover this skin
with the Rhine gold, so that not one hair remains uncovered. No other gold but the Rhine gold will do—
none but the treasure of Andvari will effect your
ransom."

Then, setting Loki free, Hreidmar told him to go
and fetch the gold while he kept the other two gods
as hostages.

Now, this treasure had been stolen by Andvari, one
of the dwarfs, from the Rhine maidens, whose duty
it had been to guard it where it lay far down in the
dim cool depths of the river. Andvari loved the precious golden stuff better than anything else in the
world. From it he had made a wonderful ring which
gave him power over every kind of precious metal.
Loki knew that he would never give up the treasure
willingly, and he made a plan to steal it from him.

Andvari often changed himself into the form of
a fish, and swam backwards and forwards over the
place where he had hidden the gold. Loki noticed
him as he swam, and guessed that it was the dwarf.
So he made a magic net, and casting it into the water
he caught Andvari in it. The fish struggled and
struggled, but Loki held him fast, until at last, changing himself into his human form, the dwarf asked him
what he would take to set him free. Loki told him
he wanted the Rhine gold, and that nothing else

would do. At first the dwarf refused to give it to him, but at last he was obliged to consent. Then, little by little, he brought up the magic treasure and laid it at Loki's feet. He would have kept back part of it, but Loki knew very well how much there ought to be. At last, when all the gold lay on the bank, he saw that the dwarf still kept on his finger the ring he had made.

" You must give me the ring too," said Loki.

Then the dwarf fell on his knees and begged that the ring, at least, might be left to him.

" You have taken all the rest," he cried; " leave me only the ring ! "

" Not one piece of gold shall you retain," said Loki, and seizing the dwarf's hand, he tore the ring roughly from his finger.

" Take it, then ! " cried Andvari furiously. " But little good shall it bring to anyone who owns it. My curse is upon it ! Death and blood shall follow its possession, until at last it shall return to the waters from whence it came."

But Loki only laughed, and taking up the golden treasure he went back to Hreidmar. Then the dwarf king brought out the otter's skin, and laying it on the ground, Loki poured out the gold upon it. Every piece of the Rhine treasure he laid on it, except the magic ring, and that he had given to Odin; but for all that there was so much of the gold, yet one little bit of the skin still remained uncovered.

" See," cried Hreidmar, " your bargain is not fulfilled ! Unless you can cover this place too, our agreement is broken, and I will not set you free."

Then Odin took the ring which Loki had given him and placed it on the spot, and when all the skin was covered Hreidmar was satisfied, and he set the gods free. But no sooner had they gone than the curse of the ring began to work. For Hreidmar had two other sons, named Regin and Fafnir, and they both cast covetous eyes upon the rich store of gold. And at last they fell upon their father and killed him for the sake of the magic treasure. And then they began to quarrel with one another, for though they could divide the gold, they could not divide the ring, and each of them wanted it for his share of the treasure. In the end, after a fierce battle, Fafnir overcame Regin and drove him away ; then, taking the gold, he carried it to the heart of a deep forest and hid it in a cavern, where he kept watch over it day and night. Once every day he was obliged to leave the treasure while he went to a stream close by to drink, but all the rest of the time he stayed at the mouth of the cavern, keeping watch in case anyone should dare to come and steal the magic gold. And because his heart grew more and more ugly and evil with gloating over the treasure, at last his outside form grew evil and ugly too, and he changed into a horrible dragon, so fierce and hideous that all who saw him shrank back in terror and fear.

But this was only the beginning of the curse. Many brave and noble men tried to kill the loathsome dragon, but Fafnir conquered them all and they perished miserably. It seemed as if misfortune fell upon everyone who even heard of the stolen treasure, and at last the gods decided that the ring must be given back to the Rhine maidens, in order that the curse might come to an end. But the gods could not touch it themselves, for they had given the gold as a ransom. The only thing they could do was to find a man strong and brave enough to kill the dragon.

There was a young man named Sigmund, who was brave and good and courageous. Odin had watched over him since he was born, and he had grown up strong and brave and manly, and at first Odin hoped that he would be found worthy to kill the dragon. He had given Sigmund a wonderful sword, before which no human being could stand; and while Sigmund had that in his possession nothing could harm him.

But Sigmund, though he was brave and good in many ways, was not quite worthy to undertake the great quest which the gods had designed for him. And one day, as he was fighting in battle, driving all before him by the might of his wonderful sword, Odin himself appeared in a cloud of light, and broke Sigmund's sword into two pieces, so that Sigmund was left defenceless in the midst of his enemies, who set upon him and killed him.

But though Sigmund was dead he left behind him his little baby son, a boy named Sigurd. And when, soon after, Sigmund's wife was married again to a great king, Sigurd was brought up at the king's court as his own son. The lad grew up tall and straight and fair, and he was so brave and fearless that everybody guessed that he would be a great warrior in time to come. And the king, his foster-father, determined to send the boy to some man who was skilled in craftsmanship of war to be trained in feats of arms.

Now it happened that Regin, the son of the dwarf-king, after he had been driven away by his brother Fafnir, had come to the court where Sigurd was being brought up. Here he had become a smith, and because he was very skilful in forging weapons, he soon won great fame in the land. And the king sent Sigurd to Regin to be trained in feats of arms, for he thought that the clever smith was the best man to teach his foster-son all that he ought to know.

Regin was very glad when Sigurd was sent to him. He saw how brave and strong the lad was, and soon a plan came into his head by which he could use the boy's strength to gain his own ends. He was still covetous of the treasure which his brother Fafnir, in the form of a hideous dragon, guarded in the depths of the forest, and he thought that when Sigurd was grown up he would be able to persuade him to kill the dragon, and then he, Regin, would gain the treasure for his own.

When the time came for Sigurd to leave him, Regin told the young man about the dragon, and Sigurd, fired with enthusiasm, made up his mind to kill the monster.

"Make me a sword, then," he cried, "and I will surely slay this evil beast."

So Regin set to work to make Sigurd a sword. He used all his craft in the making of it, but when it was done, Sigurd raised it in his hands and smote it upon the steel anvil in Regin's workshop, and the sword was shattered to pieces.

"That is no good to kill a dragon with," said Sigurd.

The Curse of Andvari's Gold

Then Regin set to work again, and again he forged a splendid sword which seemed as though it could have no flaw in it. But again when Sigurd tried it upon the anvil it broke to bits. Many other weapons did Regin make, but none of them could stand the test to which Sigurd put them.

Now Sigurd's mother had kept the broken pieces of the magic sword which Odin had given to Sigurd's father, and at last Sigurd, in despair of finding a weapon strong enough to kill the dragon, went to his mother and asked her to give him the pieces of his father's sword. Then he carried them to Regin's forge.

"Make me a sword of these," he said, and Regin set to work to make another sword.

And this time, when the sword was finished and Sigurd raised it in his hands and smote with all his strength upon the anvil, the weapon did not break. Instead, the anvil was cleft from the top to the bottom, so great was the sharpness of the magic blade.

Now at last Sigurd had found a weapon to satisfy him, and armed with the sword he set out to kill the dragon. He had a terrible fight, but in the end he killed the monster, and so once more Andvari's curse was fulfilled, and the ring for which Fafnir had killed his father was the cause of Fafnir's death as well.

When Regin saw that Fafnir was dead he was overjoyed. Now he had only to get rid of Sigurd, and the treasure he had coveted so long would be his. But there was still something else he wanted which only Sigurd could get for him, and that was the dragon's heart, which possessed such magic power that whoever ate of it would be able to understand the language of birds. Only Sigurd's sword was sharp enough to cut out the dragon's heart, so before he tried to kill the young man Regin told him to roast the dragon's heart for him in order that he might eat it.

Sigurd hastened to obey, for as yet he did not know what a false friend Regin was to him.

He cut out the heart of the dragon and began to roast it at the fire, but as it was cooking he happened to burn his fingers against it so severely that he put them to his mouth to soothe the pain. And at once, as soon as the blood of the dragon's heart touched his tongue, he heard voices all about him, and he found that he understood the language of the birds.

As he listened he found that they were talking about himself and Regin.

"How foolish is Sigurd to sit there roasting the heart for Regin, who is only plotting to kill him!" they said. "Why does he not eat of the heart himself? Then he would understand the wicked thoughts that are in Regin's mind."

When Sigurd heard these words he rose up and turned angrily to Regin.

"Would you so kill me?" he cried in a passion. And drawing his sword he smote Regin on the head, so that he fell to the ground and died. So the ring had already wrought three deaths. Three men had already died because of it—Hreidmar, Fafnir, and now Regin, who had held it in his possession for such a short time.

The Curse of Andvari's Gold

Now that he had killed Regin the great treasure belonged to Sigurd. He gathered it up and placed it on the back of his horse, and on his finger he put the fateful ring; then he set out on his journey into the world to seek adventure. For he thought he would not go back to the court of his foster-father until he had earned for himself a great name.

As he journeyed on he heard the birds twittering in the trees above him, and now that he could understand what they were saying, he listened intently. And he heard them say that far away, on the top of a lofty mountain, there lay a maiden fast asleep in a ring of fire, waiting until the man should come who would be strong enough and brave enough to break through the flames and claim her as his bride. And when Sigurd heard of the beauty of this maiden, he made up his mind to ride to the mountain and see if he could not win her for his wife.

For many long days and nights he rode, and at last he reached the mountain and found all as the birds had said.

The flames rose up fierce and strong around the sleeping maiden, but Sigurd, who had killed the dragon, was not afraid of them. He plunged boldly into the heart of the fire, and found, to his astonishment, that the flames had no power to scorch him, and he passed through them unhurt.

In the charmed circle of the flames lay what seemed to be the body of a mail-clad warrior, covered with an immense shield. But when Sigurd had lifted the shield he found that it covered the most beautiful maiden he had ever seen. He gazed at her in awe and love and wonder, and as he gazed a sudden longing sprang up in his heart, and bending down he gently kissed the beautiful face.

No sooner had his lips touched hers than the maiden awoke and sat up with a cry of gladness.

" At last you have come ! " she cried, and Sigurd, looking upon her now that she was awake, saw that she was even more beautiful than she had seemed in her sleep.

Then Brunhilde—for that was her name—told Sigurd how she had come to fall asleep within the circle of fire. She had once been one of the Valkyrie, or war-maidens, who lived in the halls of Valhalla, and rode forth to carry to Asgard the souls of the heroes who were slain in battle. But once Brunhilde had disobeyed Odin's commands, and he had condemned her to become a mortal maiden, and had said that she must go down to earth to wed like other mortal maidens. Brunhilde told Sigurd how frightened she had been lest she should be obliged to marry a coward, and how at last Odin had decreed she should lie asleep surrounded by a living wall of flame, to wait the coming of a man without fear, who alone could force his way through the flames. And so, for many long years, she had lain there, waiting for the coming of the hero who should awaken her from sleep.

For a long time Sigurd and Brunhilde talked together, falling more and more in love with each other all the while. Sigurd wanted to marry Brunhilde at once, but Brunhilde, who admired courage in a man more than anything else, would not consent to his abandoning all his hope of adventure for her sake.

The Curse of Andvari's Gold

"Go forth," she said, "and gain fresh victories, and when you have performed your share of knightly deeds, then come back to me and I will go with you wheresoever you will. Until you return I will await you here, surrounded by the wall of fire which none but you may penetrate."

Then Sigurd placed Andvari's ring on Brunhilde's finger, and tenderly saying good-bye, he led his horse through the flames and set out once more on his quest for adventures.

After many days he came to a beautiful castle that stood on the banks of the Rhine river. Here lived a king and queen, who had three brave sons and one beautiful daughter, and when Sigurd came to the castle gate they welcomed him kindly. But the queen was learned in the ways of witchcraft, and when she knew that Sigurd was the slayer of the dragon and the owner of Andvari's treasure, she began to plot and plan how she might marry him to her daughter, and so bring the vast hoard of gold into the family for ever.

Gudrun, her daughter, had fallen in love with the brave, handsome young hero as soon as she set eyes upon him; but Sigurd could not love her, for he could think and talk of no one else but Brunhilde.

But the queen made a magic drink which she gave to Sigurd, and when he had drunk it he no longer remembered the beautiful maiden to whom he was pledged. All memory of the dragon he had slain and the gold that was his vanished from his mind, and he fell in love with Gudrun, who was fair and good, and who did not know of her mother's treachery.

Very soon Sigurd was married to Gudrun, and

215

then for a long time he lived at the court of the king. He was happy, but sometimes in the midst of all his happiness he seemed to remember something which he knew would make him sad if ever the full memory came back to him. But the queen's magic drink had been so powerful, that, strive as he would, he could never quite remember what it was that was troubling him.

After a time the old king died, and his eldest son, a brave and handsome prince named Gunnar, succeeded to the throne. Gunnar was not married, and his mother, the queen, wished to see him with a wife who should be worthy of his high estate. By her magic powers she knew all about the beautiful maiden guarded by the flames of fire, and she told Gunnar to ride forth to win Brunhilde for his wife.

Gunnar rode forth eagerly enough, but he could not force his way through the flames. Only one man could ever do that, and Gunnar was not he. So he went back and told his mother, and the queen called Sigurd to her and asked him to undertake the quest for Gunnar's sake. Sigurd willingly agreed, for he and Gunnar were like brothers together, and the queen enchanted him so that in face and figure he appeared to be Gunnar, and no man might know the difference between them.

Then Sigurd rode forth, and once more the flames gave way before him; and reaching Brunhilde's side he lifted her in his arms and carried her away. Brunhilde was sorely frightened, for she had thought that no one would ever pierce the flames save Sigurd.

" Who are you ? " she cried tremblingly ; and Sigurd, who could not remember his own past, and who was only eager to persuade the maiden to marry Gunnar, answered :

" I am King Gunnar, and I have come from my own country far away to win you for my wife."

Poor Brunhilde was nearly broken hearted, for she loved Sigurd dearly, and had been longing for the time when he should come to claim her for his bride. But there was no help for it, for she had vowed to marry the man who should succeed in carrying her through the ring of fire. She pulled from her finger the ring which Sigurd had given her, and promised to marry Gunnar ; then the two set out together towards Gunnar's kingdom.

When they reached the castle Sigurd gave Brunhilde into the charge of the waiting maids who came out to meet them, while he himself hurried to the queen, who quickly disenchanted him so that he regained his own form. Then Gunnar hastened out to meet Brunhilde, whom he joyfully claimed as his bride, and the wedding took place at once.

But after the wedding, when Brunhilde was brought into the hall of the castle, she suddenly came face to face with Sigurd.

" Sigurd ! Sigurd ! " she cried. But Sigurd did not know her, and only gazed at her with wondering, puzzled eyes. Then Brunhilde caught sight of the ring upon his finger, and thinking that Sigurd was deceiving her and only pretending not to know her, she turned from him in heart-broken silence, and followed her husband to the feast.

But Sigurd had told his wife how he had won Brunhilde for Gunnar, and one day Gudrun told the whole story to Brunhilde. Brunhilde was furious at the way she had been deceived, and she was very grieved, too, to think that she had broken the vow she had made to wed none save the man who could force his way through the flames. For many days she would see no one. She shut herself up in her room and mourned and wept, and then she went to her husband and told him that he must put Sigurd to death, that she might be released from her vow.

Gunnar loved Sigurd, and he could not bear to put him to death. But he loved Brunhilde too, and in the end his love for his wife triumphed over his love for his friend. But he could not do the deed himself, so he persuaded his younger brother to do it for him.

The next day the whole party went out hunting, and Gudrun and Brunhilde rode with them too. Sigurd was gay and happy, for he had grown very fond of Gudrun, and his life seemed to stretch far before him, prosperous and bright. He did not know that Gunnar and his brothers had planned his death, and that the ring he wore on his finger must surely bring his doom.

Suddenly, as he rode, laughing and talking, one of the king's brothers pierced his heart with a spear, and the hero fell forward on the ground, dying. And when Brunhilde saw him lying there all her desire for vengeance fled from her heart, and springing to Sigurd's side, she lifted his head on her lap and called to him in loving tones.

And as Sigurd looked up at her with dying eyes, the spell which the queen had laid upon him was suddenly broken. He remembered her now, and lifting his arms he tried to draw her to him.

" Brunhilde—Brunhilde—it is you I love—only you ! " he said, and then Brunhilde, her heart breaking with grief and sorrow, realised that he had never meant to slight her ; he had only fallen a victim to the schemes of others.

Willingly would she have given her life to save Sigurd's if it had been possible, but it was too late. The curse of the ring had power even over the hero who had rescued it from the dragon, and as she called his name despairingly, Sigurd raised himself in her arms, and calling out " Brunhilde—Brunhilde ! " fell back dead.

Gunnar, who had stood by watching, came and looked down at the dead hero's body. He was overcome with remorse for the part he had played in the tragedy, and he told Brunhilde all that he knew of Sigurd's coming and the cup of forgetfulness which had been given to him to drink. And Brunhilde, as she learnt how innocent and blameless Sigurd had been all through, became more and more sorrowful.

Gudrun, who had loved Sigurd devotedly, was almost as unhappy as she was, and it was a sad and silent party that returned in mourning to the castle.

The next day a huge funeral pyre was built on the banks of the river, and Sigurd's body was laid upon it, and then with weeping and mourning the attendants set fire to the faggots.

As the flames rose high into the air Brunhilde suddenly sprang forward and flung herself upon Sigurd's body, determining to die with him rather than live without him. The fire burnt up fiercely and still more fiercely, until at last the mortal bodies of the two who had loved each other so dearly were burned to ashes and their immortal souls rose up into the sky. Then out of the river there came a great wave which, rising high over the bank, swept down upon the fire and extinguished the flames. And as the water swept back into the river, one of the Rhine maidens was seen holding aloft the ring which had been the cause of so much trouble.

And so the curse of Andvari's gold was ended.

"King Midas has great Ass's Ears!"

MIDAS was a king who lived in the days when gods and goddesses often walked about the earth, and when the great god Pan roamed amongst the woods and wild places. Midas had often heard Pan playing upon his pipes, and he admired the god's music very much, and often told him that he could play better than anyone else in the world. And in time Pan became very proud of his playing and the power it gave him over the woodland creatures. He even began to think that he must be a better musician than Apollo himself, the god of music, and one day he challenged Apollo to a contest to decide which was the better player.

King Midas was to be the judge. After Pan had finished playing he called him to his side and said that the prize must surely be his, since nobody in the world could hope to play better than he did. But then Apollo stepped forward, and, lifting his lyre, he made such wonderful music that all the people who had gathered round to listen to the contest held their breath with pleasure. As the god played on, his audience laughed and cried in turn as the music rippled with happiness or wailed in sorrow; and when he had finished they clustered around him with cries of praise and crowned him with a wreath of his favourite laurel leaves.

And Pan himself, the great god Pan, flung down his pipe and declared that Apollo had indeed won the contest, and that he was hopelessly beaten.

But King Midas was angry to think that his favourite Pan had been beaten, and he still declared that Pan's music was the best, although everybody knew that it could not be compared to Apollo's. And when he still kept on persisting that Apollo could not play as well as Pan, the sun-god grew angry too, and to punish King Midas for his foolish judgment he made long ass's ears grow on each side of his head.

King Midas was terribly dismayed when he found what had happened. He hurried to his bedchamber and locked himself in and sent for the court barber, whom he told to make him a wig so that none of his subjects should know what had happened to their king. The barber made a splendid wig which quite covered the dreadful ears, and then the king sent him away after making him promise, on pain of instant death if he broke his word, never to tell to any human being that the king possessed a pair of ass's ears.

The barber gave his promise, and then he hurried back to his home in a great state of fear. He was dreadfully afraid, poor man, lest he should let the secret out to anyone by accident; and at last he began to worry over it so that he felt that unless he could speak out and ease his mind he would go mad with the difficulty of keeping silence.

So one night he stole out of the town and went far away into a great lonely field. There he dug a deep hole in the ground, and lying down beside it he said in a loud whisper:

"King Midas has great Ass's Ears"

" King Midas has great ass's ears! King Midas has great ass's ears! "

Then he filled up the hole and went home, feeling ever so much better now that he had at last got rid of his terrible secret.

The days and weeks and months went by, and over the hole which the barber had dug there sprang up a clump of hollow reeds, and as the wind rustled over them a strange murmur came from their slender stems—a murmur which grew and grew until at last there came forth these words :

" King Midas has great ass's ears! King Midas has great ass's ears! "

So the secret was out. Everybody who passed that way heard the murmur of the reeds. People talked about it in the city, flowers whispered it to one another, and the wind carried the tidings through the world :

" King Midas has great ass's ears! King Midas has great ass's ears! "

But King Midas could not punish the barber, for the poor man had not told the secret to a single living person.

The Goddess of the Moon

DIANA, the goddess of the moon, was Apollo's twin sister. In the daytime she came down to earth and, accompanied by her maidens, wandered through the woods with her bow and arrow, for she was a great huntress, and was famed for her skill in shooting. But every night, when her brother's golden chariot sank to rest in the western sea, Diana mounted her silver car and drove her milk-white steeds across the sky. And as she drove she often bent down to look at the earth, which seemed to her to be even more beautiful by night than it was by day.

One night, as she was driving, she saw a young shepherd lying on a hillside fast asleep. His face was raised to the sky, and as the moonlight fell upon it Diana held her breath in wonder, for she thought she had never seen so beautiful a face before. And yielding to a sudden impulse, the goddess sprang from her chariot, and, bending over the sleeping boy, kissed his parted lips. Then she hastened back to her silver car and sailed once more upon her way.

Endymion—for that was the shepherd's name—awoke with a start. It seemed to him that a lovely woman, more lovely than he had ever imagined a woman could be, had come to him in his sleep and

224

kissed him. When he looked round and found himself alone, he thought it was only a dream; but it was such a beautiful one that every night after that he went to the hillside and lay down there to sleep, hoping that he might dream the dream again. And every night, as Diana drove by, she descended from her car and bent to kiss him in his sleep.

For many nights this happened. Endymion grew more and more in love with the beautiful vision that came to him in his dreams, and he looked forward eagerly to the night-time, which brought him such great happiness.

But the goddess Diana grew sad and sorrowful; she could not bear to think that this beautiful boy must one day grow old and careworn, and be bowed down with all the grief and pain which fall to the lot of mortal men, and at last she thought of a way to save him from all this unhappiness.

She caused an eternal sleep to fall upon Endymion, and, lifting him in her arms, she carried him away to a secret cave in a high mountain. And there Endymion sleeps on for ever, always young and beautiful, dreaming happy dreams of love and joy and beauty.

And every night, when Diana drives her car across the sky, she stops for one moment when she reaches the mountain-top to bend down and kiss the sleeping boy.

The Quest of the Golden Fleece

IT was in the days of the great heroes that there was born in Thessaly a boy who, while yet a babe, was cast out upon the mountains to perish. A wild mare coming along kicked the child and bruised his face so that it was black as night. Had it not been that shortly afterwards a poor shepherd found him, and took him to his home in the mountains, the deserted baby would have died. But, as it was, he lived, and, because of his blackened face, he was called Pelias.

Now, Pelias was brought up by the shepherd as his son, and he grew strong and fierce, as though the wild winds of the mountains which had blown upon him when he lay forgotten as a babe had entered into him. He cared not for law, and gathered around him when he became a man all the fearless and lawless men of Thessaly, by whose aid he drove from the throne of Iolcus King Æson, who was stepbrother to Pelias.

1.—HOW JASON SET OUT FOR HIS KINGDOM

ÆSON took his young son and left him in the care of Cheiron, the Centaur, lest Pelias should kill him. In the goodly company of the heroes who lived with the Cen-

The Quest of the Golden Fleece

taur, the wisest of creatures, the boy dwelt ten years.
He grew a strong and comely youth, and was able to
run and swim, to wrestle and box, to shoot straight and
true with arrow and bow, was an adept on horseback, a
sweet singer of songs, and wise in the use of herbs
against disease. Because of this latter gift was he
named Jason, or " the Healer."

In those ten years Jason forgot all about the early
days in Iolcus, forgot, too, that once his father was a
king, and that in his, Jason's, place there now reigned
in Iolcus a usurper. But the time came when his play-
fellows went out into the world to win fame and
honour ; and Jason longed to go forth too.

One day Cheiron found him gazing upon the plains of
Thessaly, and learnt that he had heard something of
the story of the kingdom that had been his father's.
Jason wanted to go at once and wrest it from the
usurper.

Cheiron told him that Pelias was a mighty man,
who would not lightly part with what he held, and
that ere he could sit upon the throne of Iolcus
Jason must pass through dangers the like of which no
man had had to face.

" I care not ! " cried Jason. " To Iolcus I will
go."

Cheiron, seeing that the youth was not to be dissuaded from his purpose, sent him forth with his
blessing.

Thus it was that Jason the Healer, whose heart was
kind, who spoke naught but what was true, nor did
aught but what was good, began the wanderings of
many years.

2.—THE COMING OF THE MAN WITH ONE SANDAL

WHILE Jason was living with Cheiron King Pelias was ruling the kingdom he had obtained; but not even riches and power could make him altogether happy. For an oracle had told him that one day there should come to Iolcus a son of the House of Æolus, a man wearing but one sandal, who should take away from Pelias the kingdom. Pelias feared the coming of such a man. And the time drew near when the words of the oracle were to be proved true.

When Jason left Cheiron he went on until he came to the rushing torrent of Anauros, swollen by heavy rains. To a less determined and a weaker man it would have proved impassable, but Jason leapt boldly in, and, fighting, struggling against the current, which threatened to cast him upon the rocks, he came at last to the farther bank. He lay awhile resting, and then, feeling refreshed, set out on his way once more.

But the leaping waters of Anauros had claimed one of his sandals; and Jason knew that he must continue his journey with one foot bare.

Entering the plains of Thessaly, Jason came to the city of Iolcus. He walked about the streets seeking the palace of the king, and so intent was he that he did not notice how folks stared at him, and whispered to one another. It had been many a day since a man so beautiful, and seemingly so strong, had come to Iolcus; and, moreover, this giant youth wore but one sandal. And the people of the city remembered what the oracle had said.

228

The Quest of the Golden Fleece

Presently an old man stopped Jason and asked him his name, and what he sought.

"I am Jason, come from Mount Pelion," said the youth, "and I seek the palace of King Pelias, with whom I would speak."

The old man looked at him for a moment, and then asked him if he had not heard of the oracle.

"It is no small danger that you run, my son, in walking about the streets of Iolcus wearing but one sandal!"

When Jason heard what the man said he rejoiced, for had he not left the cave of Cheiron in order that he might win back his kingdom? Why, then, should he be afraid?

So he told the people of Iolcus, who did not love Pelias, for he was a harsh ruler; and they talked amongst themselves when they saw Jason go to the palace of the king. Pelias, when he saw the youth, trembled; for the one-sandalled man had come!

"Who are you?" he demanded.

"I am Jason, thy nephew, and heir to this kingdom!" said Jason boldly.

And Pelias, being crafty, professed to be pleased that his nephew had come to Iolcus, though in his heart he resolved that in some way he would get rid of Jason.

That night Pelias gave a great feast in honour of Jason, and, having thought of a way by which he might rid himself of the youth's presence, told him the story of the Golden Fleece.

This is the story that King Pelias told Jason.

3.—THE STORY OF THE GOLDEN FLEECE

MANY years before King Athamas, of Orchomenos, had taken as his second wife Ino, who hated the children of the first wife, Nephele, because she knew that they had claim to the kingdom before her own children. She therefore plotted to destroy Nephele's children, Phrixus and Helle, and her opportunity came when a great famine spread over the land. King Athamas sent to the oracle asking advice on how to bring back the days of golden fields. The priests of the oracle had been bribed by Queen Ino, and told Athamas that no fat years would come unless he sacrificed Nephele's children. Athamas, for his people's sake, said he would do this dread thing, and the boy and girl were brought to the altar.

But Queen Nephele, although she had left the land, had not forgotten her children, and besought the gods to save them. Thus it came about that just when the sacrifice was going to be made the assembled people saw a great cloud appear in the sky, and from out of it there descended a beautiful golden ram, with wings on its back. It rested upon the altar, and instantly Phrixus and Helle stretched out their hands and grasped its Golden Fleece.

Then up into the air rose the ram, flying away towards the sea, while Athamas knew that the priests had not told the truth—else why had the gods snatched the sacrifice from the very altar ? He was angry, and, turning upon Ino and her children, took vengeance.

The Quest of the Golden Fleece

Meanwhile, the ram with the Golden Fleece was winging its way northward, until it came to the sea, the children clinging to it. Poor little Helle by this time had grown tired. She lost her hold, fell into the shining sea below and was drowned; and from that day the sea there has been called the Hellespont. Phrixus, scared at what had happened to his sister, clung tighter to the Fleece, and at last the ram came to earth at Colchis, on the shore of the Euxine Sea.

Here Phrixus stayed, and in due course married the daughter of the king, sacrificing the ram as a thank-offering to the gods. The Golden Fleece was nailed to a tree, and a fierce dragon was placed at the foot of the tree to guard it by night and day.

"Phrixus died," Pelias said then, "but even in death he remembers the land of Hellas, and would return to it, yet cannot. He haunts me in my dreams and implores that I fetch the Golden Fleece from the beech tree in Colchis, for with it his spirit will return to Hellas. But there are dangers untold awaiting him who would fetch the Golden Fleece."

And Jason, looking at his uncle, knew that he was a craven at heart, else why did he not go? But he said nothing, for Pelias had changed the conversation, and was saying that in Iolcus he had an enemy whom he feared, although he could still give orders to him, seeing that he was the stronger for a while.

"Tell me, Jason," the king said, "what you would do to get rid of such a man?"

And Jason, whose thoughts still ran on the Golden Fleece, replied:

"I would send him to bring me the Golden Fleece,

231

seeing that the dangers are many and that he might never return ! "

" You speak well, my son," Pelias answered. " It shall be done."

The way in which Pelias spoke made Jason realise at last that the king was referring to him, but, being true at heart, and a man who never took back what he said, he jumped to his feet and cried :

" I see now your trick, yet will I go forth and fetch the Golden Fleece. Promise me that the day I bring it my kingdom shall be given back."

And Pelias, who feared the youth who had come as the oracle had said, gave his word, yet hoped that the perils of the great quest might overwhelm Jason.

4.—THE BUILDING OF THE SHIP

NEXT day Jason began his work of preparation. He consulted the oracle, who advised him to get Argus, the wonderful builder of ships, to make him a boat. He was also to gather around him the heroes of Hellas, many of whom had been his own playmates on Mount Pelion.

Jason sent heralds, who cried in the cities and the wild places, saying :

" Who dares to venture with Jason for the Golden Fleece ? "

And the heroes heard the call, and hearing came down to Iolcus to join Jason, so that he found himself with a goodly company of nine and forty. Amongst them were Pollux the boxer, and his brother, Castor ;

The Quest of the Golden Fleece

Peleus, the father of Achilles ; Piphys the steersman ; Zetès and Calaïs, the sons of the north wind ; and many another, including Orpheus, the sweet singer.

Then the work of building the ship began ; the forests were robbed of their finest pines, which the heroes dragged down to the beach, where they shaped them with axes, and made them into the finest ship the world had ever seen. Fifty oars she was to take, one for each of the heroes ; they covered her with pitch to keep out the water, and they painted her a bright red. Then they called her Argo, after her builder, and they themselves were known as the Argonauts.

But when she was ready not all the efforts of all the heroes could launch her ; she remained fast stuck in the sand. The heroes wondered what they could do, and Orpheus took up his lyre and began to play a magic song of the sea. Music it was such as the world had never heard before ; of breaking waves, of driving winds. It stirred the echoes of the woods behind, and thrilled the hearts of the heroes who were to venture forth on a perilous quest ; and it struck upon the sides of the good ship Argo, which seemed to answer to it, and—wonder of wonders—which moved, nay, leaped like a white horse of the sea, and plunged into the water !

Jason's gallant band, having provisioned her, got into the ship, and the people of Iolcus, including King Pelias, watched them as they bent their backs to the mighty oars and swept out of the harbour across the wide sea.

The quest of the Golden Fleece had begun.

5.—THE HARPIES, AND THE WANDERING ROCKS

THE adventures of the heroes began very soon, for
when they arrived at a certain land the king, Amycus,
refused them hospitality. So Pollux the boxer went
ashore to teach him manners. Now Amycus was a
mighty fighter who overcame all who opposed him;
but this time he met his match, and very soon Pollux
had put an end to him, and after refreshing themselves
the Argonauts boarded their vessel again and swept
through the seas to the city of Salmydessus, where King
Phineus reigned. Phineus was blind, poor man, having
been afflicted thus through offending Jupiter, who, to
make his punishment more complete, had caused three
fierce and terrible birds to haunt him. These birds,
which were called Harpies, had the heads of women and
the bodies and wings and claws of vultures, and whenever
Phineus sat down to meals they would swoop down
and seize the food. So strong and terrible were they
that not all the king's men could do anything against
them, with the result that Phineus was wellnigh starved
to death.

When Jason and his companions came to Salmydessus, Phineus told them of his woes; and the heroes
asked that they might sit with him and eat. Phineus
bade them welcome, but no sooner had the feast begun
than the Harpies appeared. Instantly every hero was
upon his feet and seeking to wound or kill the Harpies,
whom, however, they could not touch.

When it seemed that nothing could be done, up flew
the winged sons of the north wind, Zetès and Calaïs.

The Quest of the Golden Fleece

They swooped down upon the Harpies, who, unused to being attacked in this way, fled, pursued by the two brothers. Over the land and out to sea the two heroes chased the Harpies, who at last grew so tired that they could not keep up, and, filled with fear, fell into the sea and were drowned.

The sons of the north wind took back to King Phineus the glad news, and while the Argonauts stayed at Salmydessus they were fêted by the people. Then the day came when the Argo must be off again, and Phineus, who knew whither they were bound, told them that Jupiter had placed in the Euxine Sea two Wandering Rocks to guard the way to Colchis.

"Take heed of the Wandering Rocks," said Phineus, "for woe be to the ship which gets caught between them when they meet, as happens whenever a ship tries to pass. Even a fish that tries to swim by, or a bird that seeks to fly between them is crushed to death. But, know this, that so soon as the rocks have dashed against each other, they sweep apart, and leave a wide space, so that a cunning steersman may get his ship past !"

The Argonauts thanked King Phineus for his counsel and went on their way. Many adventures they met, till they came into the Euxine Sea, into which no Greek had ever before ventured ; a sea of unknown dangers.

As they voyaged into this sea the winds blew cold upon them and a storm swept down, while straight before them the Wandering Rocks, shining like glass, reared their glittering pinnacles, and seemed to be hurrying towards each other—as though they would warn the mariners. But the Argonauts, profiting by the advice of King Phineus, had prepared against this. As soon as they came close to the rocks, one of them loosed a pure white dove he held ; away it flew. While the Argonauts watched, they saw her fly between the rocks, which came crashing together. But the dove, befriended by the gods, succeeded in getting through, suffering only the loss of her tail, that was caught by the rocks, which immediately flew apart again.

This was what the Argonauts had waited for, and Piphys, at the helm, called on them to bend to the oars ; the Argo cut through the waters, sending great showers of foam all about her, and, ere ever the rocks could come together again, had slipped through the opening.

6.—IN THE LAND OF THE GOLDEN FLEECE

COLCHIS, the Land of the Golden Fleece, was still far away, and before the Argonauts arrived there they had many other adventures, of which, however, there is no time to tell now. One day, as they sailed to the east, they saw the snowcapped Caucasus, and, coming closer, saw the glittering roofs of the palaces of King Æetes, who ruled over Colchis ; and they knew that they were come to the Land of the Golden Fleece.

Jason and Pollux went straight up to the palace and asked to see the king. Jason told Æetes why he had come, and the king, who knew that an oracle had said that one day a man out of Greece should come for the Golden Fleece, sought to put off the time when he must give it up.

236

The Quest of the Golden Fleece

Therefore, he told Jason that he should have it, but that he must do certain things before he should be allowed to take it away.

"Tell me, sir," said Jason, "what these things be, that I may be up and doing."

"First," answered King Æetes, "you must harness and tame my fiery bulls, yoke them to a plough, and plough a certain field, which you must then sow with dragon's teeth! After that there is the sleepless dragon who guards the Fleece night and day—he must be overcome."

Task enough for any man! For the bulls were strong, and had brazen horns and hoofs, while their breath was fire; and the dragon's teeth that Jason was to sow would give a harvest of armed iron men who, springing up from the ground, would fall upon him who had sown the seed!

King Æetes hoped that either the brazen bulls or the iron men would kill Jason, and so save for a while the Golden Fleece for Colchis. But Jason, although he knew the dangers that lay before him, agreed to pit his strength against the brazen bulls, and, if successful, to plough the field and sow the dragon's teeth.

7.—THE BRAZEN BULLS, AND THE DRAGON'S TEETH

WHAT might have happened to the fearless youth had he gone at once to the task of taming the bulls, it is impossible to say; but while he had been speaking with King Æetes, the latter's daughter, Medea, had been standing by, and had fallen in love with the youth from Hellas. She was a witch, who knew the uses of all the herbs that grew, and she made up her mind that she would help Jason if he would marry her.

So when Jason left the palace of the king the king's daughter followed him, and promised that she would make him the strongest of men for one day. She gave him a magic potion, which he was to rub on his hands and face, his arms and legs, and his shield and sword and lance. Not only would he be so strong, but he would also find that ice could not freeze him, nor fire burn, nor any weapon pierce his armour, while his own good sword and lance would be able to pierce iron as easily as a stick dips into water.

So it came about that when Jason went to harness the brazen bulls and sow the dragon's teeth, he was well equipped, and feared naught. All the people of Colchis had gathered together where they could watch the hero. Jason, having used the magic potion as Medea had told him, went boldly to the door of the stable which housed the bulls, flung it wide open, and entered. King Æetes looked on and laughed scornfully, for he knew how terrible were his bulls. But Jason stepped up to the bulls, unfastened the iron chains that bound them, seized them each by one horn, and, plunge though they did, and stamp their hoofs upon the ground, while their nostrils breathed fire which it seemed must consume the brave youth, he led them out into the view of the assembled people.

Then Jason pitted himself against the brazen bulls, and the people, looking on, wondered at the marvellous thing they saw; this youth from Hellas so nimbly escaping the trampling hoofs, so fearless of the raging fire that leapt from the nostrils of the bulls. And although they wondered, they told themselves that there could be but one end to it, i.e. Jason must be killed. Imagine, then, their surprise when, after a long and fearsome struggle, the brazen bulls were forced to their knees.

What shouts went up, what cheers! And what anger filled the heart of King Æetes! But although his bulls had been defeated, yet he still hoped that the sowing of the dragon's teeth would bring about the destruction of Jason, and he waited anxiously while Jason held the bulls down to the ground and Pollux yoked them to the plough. Then, springing out of the way, Jason seized the iron chain with one hand, and with the other the handle of the plough.

As soon as the bulls felt the youth's hands gone from their horns, they leapt up, and tried to run away. But they found that a strong hand now held them in by an iron chain, and, instead of pounding off, they were forced to go quietly, dragging the plough behind them!

In this way did Jason plough the field before the eyes of the astonished people, and then when it was done, loosed the bulls, and sent them away. Afterwards he went up to King Æetes for the dragon's teeth, which he received in a helmet. Then up and down the ploughed field went Jason, sowing the teeth in the furrows the plough had made, and afterwards levelling the ground so that the teeth were covered.

Even the magic of Medea had not prevented his long day's work from making Jason weary, and when the tasks were done, about midday, he went and lay down to rest. At sunset, he returned to the field, and lo! from every furrow had sprung up armed men. Some were still held down by the feet in the ground out of which they were growing, but their arms were free, and they brandished at Jason the gleaming spears they held! Yet others, and there were many of them, had grown right out of the ground, and they, with great shouts and shaking lances and swords, rushed upon Jason.

But Jason was ready. Medea had told him a way to deal with these iron men, and he followed her advice. He picked up a huge stone, and threw it into the midst of the men racing towards him. It hit one, glanced off him, and hit another, and yet another; and in a few minutes the whole host of armed men were fighting amongst themselves, because each thought that the other had thrown the stone.

What a fight that was! One by one the iron men dropped to the ground, killed by their comrades. While this was going on, Jason, laughing to himself, went round the field, and with the sword made magical by Medea's potion cut off the heads of those warriors who had not yet grown right out of the ground!

8.—HOW JASON OBTAINED THE FLEECE

In this way were some of Jason's tasks done, and next morning he went to King Æetes to claim the right to fetch the Golden Fleece.

The king, however, was angry, and knew that unless he had been aided by some magic Jason could not have

"Straight before them the Wandering Rocks reared their glittering pinnacles"

"Galahad alone could see the perfect beauty of the Holy Grail"

accomplished the tasks. Æetes suspected that his own daughter had helped the Greek, and he made up his mind that he would burn the Argo, and destroy the heroes. He therefore told Jason to wait until next day before attacking the dragon.

Jason was willing, but Medea knew that her father suspected her, and feared that he would seek to kill Jason.

" You must kill the dragon to-night, Jason," she said, and she gave him a magic drug to use against the dragon.

That night Jason and Medea went into the grove where the Golden Fleece was nailed to the beech tree. Presently the eyes of Jason were gladdened at the sight of that which he had journeyed so far to fetch, and braved so much to claim. But for the restraining hand of Medea he would have snatched it from the tree, and so have died, for the dragon reared its head and roared.

" Throw the magic drug ! " cried Medea, and Jason threw the dragon the honey-cakes which Medea had made with the drug. Instantly the dragon snapped them up—and fell asleep ! Jason cut off its head, snatched the Golden Fleece from the tree, and together he and Medea raced through the shades of the forest until they came to the shore where lay the Argo, taking with them Absyrtus, Medea's brother.

As soon as they were on board, the Argonauts, rejoicing much at the sight of the Golden Fleece, bent to the oars and rowed out to sea, going at such a rate that King Æetes, who in the morning discovered his loss and sent his fast ships after them, could not catch them.

For one thing, Medea, when she found the king's vessels coming, threw her brother overboard, knowing that the pursuers would stay and pick him up. The Argonauts got away, but Absyrtus died.

Of the journey back to Greece there is no room to tell; but, because of Medea's wickedness in destroying her brother, the Argonauts were made to wander about the earth for many years before they could return to Iolcus.

Many were the adventures they passed through. They had been young when they set out from Iolcus, but were old when the Argo, rowed by now weakening arms, swept into the harbour again. New faces they saw, faces of the children of the men they had known in the days of old; but, in the palace, was King Pelias, old now and doddering; and with him was Æson, who in his old age had come back to the kingdom from which he had been driven.

There was much rejoicing in Iolcus when the wanderers returned, bringing with them the Golden Fleece. And Jason, thinking of all the perils that he had suffered, of all the years away from beloved Thessaly, regretted nothing—for the coming of the Fleece filled Æson with such joy that his age dropped from him, and he once more reigned in his kingdom.

The Wanderings of Ulysses

TROY, the once fair city, lay in ruins, destroyed by the Greeks of King Agamemnon, who for ten years had besieged the place; and the gods were angry with the heroes—so angry that when, their task finished, they set out for their own lands, the gods punished them in various ways.

For his part in the war Ulysses, King of Ithaca, was condemned to wander for ten years before reaching his own country—ten years of peril and adventure. Ulysses had been one of the heroes who had hidden in the wooden horse by means of which the Greeks had entered Troy; and on that day of fate he had done mighty deeds.

After the fall of Troy, Ulysses, glad to be free to leave the land of so much fighting, and with thoughts of fair Ithaca in his mind, set sail with his company of heroes.

His adventures had begun.

In their anger, the gods sent a great storm, against which the ships could not battle; and, driven by the howling wind, swamped ever and anon by the roaring waters, the spoil-laden vessels ran ashore at Ismarus, in Thrace.

Ismarus was a city whose sacking promised much booty; and Ulysses, deciding to profit out of adversity, landed his men, swept upon the town, and ransacked it of its riches.   A great haul was taken, but the Greeks outstayed their victory.   Mad with the flush of triumph, rich with their booty, they held high revel in Ismarus. They drank the wines they found, and would not leave the flowing cups when Ulysses, desiring to be on his way, warned them that the Ciconians, the people of the country, might swoop down upon them and find them unprepared for battle.

Ulysses was right; the men heeded not his warning and kept at their feasting through the night, while those of the people of Ismarus who had escaped in the sacking of the city spread the news through the land, and from far and near warriors gathered to take vengeance.

It was a mighty host which swarmed around the be-muddled Greeks, gorged with their feasting, heavy with wine—arms weakened, eyes dimmed.   The shock of battle, which came upon them all unawares, roused them somewhat from their lethargy, and for a whole day they fought against long odds—but fought hope-lessly.   The Ciconians were more than their match, and the men of Ulysses had to run for their lives to the shore, where their twelve vessels lay.   Six men out of each ship died that day in battle ; and those who escaped thanked the gods.

1.—ULYSSES AND THE LOTUS-EATERS

But the gods were not yet done with them.   The storm-god brewed a hurricane which burst upon their ships, tore their sails to ribbons, brought down the masts, and compelled them, after many days of battling with the elements, to put in to the land of the Lotus-Eaters in Libya.

To the Greeks this was a strange country, but it was a case of any port in a storm; and while a feast was being prepared scouts were sent to spy the land and to find out what kind of people lived there; the heroes were profiting by their experience at Ismarus!

It was a hospitable land; its people were gracious and generous, and the three spies had a wonderful time amongst them; in fact they were away so long that Ulysses grew anxious and set out in quest of them.

And then the secret was discovered; the land of the Lotus-Eaters was a snare. The fruit and blossoms of the lotus trees which grew in profusion were the food of the people. The juice was like nectar, and so beguiling that he who tasted it straightway lost all wish for anything but to remain in the land. Friends, home, all things were forgotten, and the eater of the lotus was tighter bound than any slave with shackles.

When Ulysses came to the place where his scouts were feasting with the Lotus-Eaters, he realised at once what peril was before him; if his men should taste the beguiling fruit he would never more see Ithaca. So, refusing the hospitality of the Lotus-Eaters, who pressed upon him their ensnaring food, the hero forbade the men with him even to touch it; and commanded them to seize and bind the scouts and bring them down to the shore.

When the boats were reached, Ulysses hurriedly embarked all his men—anxious to get them safe from temptation. The three spies soon recovered from their stupor, and were thankful to the gods for having delivered them from the snare which would have held them back from fair Ithaca.

The Greeks were in unknown seas and yet they dared not stay in that land; they had to launch their ships and bend their backs to the great sweeps which sent them—whither?

No man of them knew.

2.—ULYSSES AND POLYPHEMUS

AFTER a time the ships came in sight of the land of Cyclopes, the giants who had only one eye each, placed in the centre of their forehead. Leaving eleven of his ships beached on a little island opposite, Ulysses went over to the Cyclopes' country in order to find out something about the strange one-eyed race, and to obtain food.

The hero's galley raced through the sea, and, reaching land, Ulysses saw a huge cave in the mountainous shore.

The whole country was rich in pasturage and cattle, and the fields yielded a rich harvest without labour of man. Ulysses ran his ship ashore, and with his twelve companions entered the cave, hoping to find the owner at home—for the presence of goats and sheep betokened the fact that it was the home of one of the Cyclopes.

But, inside they found no man; only abundance of food, which they were tempted to take, but wisely left alone to await the return of the owner.

Evening drew on, and the Greeks heard the bleating of goats and sheep, the tumbling of rocks, as though flocks were coming down the mountain sides; and in a short time came one of the Cyclopes.

Standing in the darkness of the cave Ulysses and his heroes watched the giant as he herded his flocks for the night in various recesses of the cave. Then, to their alarm, the one-eyed monster closed the mouth of the cave with an enormous rock.

And the Greeks knew that they were prisoners.

They waited anxiously for the Cyclops to discover them; they dared not reveal themselves. He lighted the fire, and the glare of it penetrated throughout the cave.

Thirteen men armed with spears, swords and shields stood revealed by the blaze, and the giant, whose name was Polyphemus, and who was the fiercest and strongest of the Cyclopes, roared at them till the cave echoed and re-echoed.

"What men are you? Whence come you? Pirates who hazard your lives in the wrecking of others?"

The Greeks thrilled with the fear inspired by the monster who towered mountainously above them. Even Ulysses himself could not for a time answer him, and the men, heroes who in their time had fought and vanquished valiant foes and strong, stood trembling in the presence of the giant, whose appearance, rendered more terrible by the glaring one eye, was sufficient to strike terror into the stoutest hearts.

When the echo of Polyphemus' angry voice had rolled away, and remained little more than a murmur in the innermost depths of the cave, on whose sides the leaping flames flung fantastic shadows, Ulysses succeeded in calling up courage, and made answer to the giant that his name was " No Man "—a little joke on his part, which was to have good results later on.

He told him that he and his companions were men from the fields of Troy, driven out of their course and shipwrecked on the coast of the island of the Cyclopes. Ulysses saw that Polyphemus wanted to seize their vessel, and so decided to mislead him into believing it was smashed on the rocks.

Filled with rage, and refusing the hospitality which Ulysses asked of him, the giant seized two of the unhappy Greeks and killed and ate them ; and then he went to sleep, leaving Ulysses and his companions to spend an anxious night as best they could.

Ulysses' first impulse on seeing the giant asleep was to feel for his sword, but Polyphemus was cunning ; he had gone to sleep and left his unwilling guests at liberty and with their weapons, because he knew that if they killed him they would never be able to leave the cave —for not all the strength of Ulysses and his men would serve to roll away the great rock from the cave's mouth.

Ulysses remembered this just in time ! He decided to wait and devise some trick by which to gain liberty.

Morning came ; the giant arose, he put to death two more of Ulysses' companions, had his breakfast, and then, moving the rock, allowed his flocks to go out of the cave, and followed them, once more sealing up the opening.

Left in the cave to await the return of Polyphemus —and a dread return they knew it would be—Ulysses and his surviving companions pondered their situation, seeking some means by which to obtain their liberty.

While moving about the cave they found the giant's

club—the trunk of a huge tree—fit mast for the largest
ship ! Ulysses and his men fashioned that club into a
spear, hardening the point in the fire, and then hid it—
for Ulysses had a plan, which he meant to carry out that
very night.

Darkness fell ; the great rock was rolled away from
the cave, Polyphemus stood on guard at the entrance
while his flocks filed in ; and when the last of the animals
had entered, the giant closed the mouth and began to
prepare his meal, killing two more of the Greeks, to the
dismay of the others, who, however, had great faith in
Ulysses' scheme.

The hero, when Polyphemus had eaten his fill, approached him with a cup flowing with wine which the
adventurers had happily thought of bringing with them ;
it was strong wine which they had taken at Ismarus,
and the giant seized it and drained the cup to the very
dregs.

Polyphemus had never tasted such rare wine, and
he craved for more—called for more.

" No Man ! " he cried, " give me more of that
wonderful wine ! " and Ulysses gave him all he had,
for that was the very thing the Greeks wanted. The
wine was strong, the Cyclops greedy—and the result
was that he was very soon in a deep sleep.

That was the moment for which Ulysses had been
waiting ; the great club whose point they had sharpened
they now took from its hiding-place, heated the point
in the fire, and then stealthily approached the sleeping
giant—and the next moment had deprived the Cyclops
of his solitary eye !

With a great roar of pain Polyphemus tried to get

upon his feet, but was held down by the Greeks; the noise of his cries reached the other Cyclopes in their dwellings in other parts of the land—and, wondering what beset their friend, they strode to the mouth of the cave.

The hubbub outside was now greater than the noise inside; and the heroes trembled to think what might happen to them if Polyphemus told his fellows what was afoot.

Then a most remarkable thing happened.

" What is hurting you, Polyphemus ? " the Cyclopes cried.

" No Man ! " screamed the maddened agonising giant—" No Man hurts me ! "

The Cyclopes outside looked from one to another, and, I have no doubt, shook their heads over Polyphemus.

" No man hurts him," they said to themselves, " and yet he screams in terror ! "

" It is the hand of Jove who has brought some disease upon him," said one.

Still the giant cried aloud in his anguish, but the Cyclopes, who could get no other answer from him but that " No Man hurts me ! " told him that since that was so, he needed no help from them; and they went away !

Ulysses and his companions heard the Cyclopes retiring from the mouth of the cave and breathed freely, highly pleased that the giant in his agony had so used the name Ulysses had given that the friends had misunderstood his meaning.

It meant their salvation.

Throughout that long night Polyphemus kept in the cave, sightless and in agony, stretching his great arms

around his dwelling place, seeking to lay hands upon
the men who had taken so terrible a vengeance for
the death of their comrades. But because his one
eye had gone, the Greeks eluded him every time he
stumbled about the cave, and at last he gave up in
despair.

Ulysses had all his plans worked out ; he knew that
when the morning came Polyphemus would, if possible,
move the great rock from the cave and let out his flocks,
and the Greeks were going to seize that opportunity to
slip past the unseeing giant.

But in the morning, Polyphemus, who had cunningly
guessed that intention, rolled the rock away only
sufficiently wide for one sheep or ram at a time to pass
through, and, as each one did so, he ran his hand over
its back to assure himself that none of his captives were
riding on it !

When Ulysses saw this he was alarmed, for evidently
it would be a difficult matter to escape from so wily a
captor. He and his friends whispered together, seeking
a way of outwitting Polyphemus. At last they hit upon
an idea.

If they could not ride upon the backs of the rams,
they could try clinging to them underneath ! So,
Ulysses helped each of his companions as they tied
themselves to the undersides of the rams, and then he
himself, seizing the largest ram of all—it was the
favourite ram of Polyphemus—clung to the fleece and
waited for the time to come when they all must pass
before the giant.

One by one they reached the opening in the
cave ; one by one Polyphemus ran his hands along

the backs of the rams, and feeling no one there let them go through the mouth of the place.

And then came Ulysses; and his heart stood still as Polyphemus, with his hand on the back of the ram, held it awhile. He recognised the fleece as that of his pet, who had been wont to be among the first out of the cave every morning, and he wondered why on this occasion it should be last! Ulysses had not known this, or he would have seen that it went earlier! The hero waited with bated breath—waited for the time when he would get past the giant. Would he be discovered?

It was a relieved Ulysses who heard Polyphemus tell the ram to go—and in a moment the hero was outside the cave—free. Quickly he got loose from the ram, and singled out the animals bearing his friends, whom he released, and the little company of survivors out of thirteen who had set out rushed down to the shore, embarked in their boat, and rowed away from the land.

Well away from the shore the Greeks rested upon their oars, and Ulysses, in a loud voice, cried out to Polyphemus, who was wandering about disconsolately, and taunted him for his inhospitality, revealing at the same time the real name of the man who had put out his eye. The giant, furious at the ruse which had been played upon him, tore at the great rocks on the mountains and flung them far out to sea in the direction from which the taunting voice of Ulysses came.

Gigantic pieces of rock fell into the sea, sending up volumes of water, and causing the sea to heave as if at the bidding of the winds, and so great was the surge of the waters that the ship was flung back upon the shore.

The Wanderings of Ulysses

The Greeks bent their oars and pulled hard against the tide, sweeping the boat out into the sea again. Only just in time did they get away, for a huge piece of rock came hurtling through the air—to fall into the sea, scraping the boat as it did so.

After so narrow an escape Ulysses did not venture to stay any longer to taunt the foe, and the survivors rowed back to where they had left their companions in the other ships.

3.—THE WINDS OF ÆOLUS

IN due course the Greeks resumed their wanderings at sea, and came to the Æolian Islands, where Æolus, king of the wind, held sway.

Ulysses was received kindly here, and stayed for a month in Æolus, spending his time in telling the king all that had happened at the siege of Troy. When the Greeks departed, Æolus, to give them a good voyage, confined all the adverse winds in a leathern bag, which he hung in Ulysses' ship.

Thus helped by the friendly winds which Æolus caused to blow upon them, the ships ran onward—towards Ithaca. Nine days of such voyaging brought the wanderers in sight of home. But the gods had not yet done with Ulysses. While he slept—the first time in many days—his companions, thinking that it must contain something rich and wonderful, opened the bag containing the contrary winds. Instantly a hurricane blew which took them in its swirling arms and bore them away from Ithaca back to Æolus,

253

where, hungry and thirsty (for all their food had gone) they jumped ashore and went to see the king.

The hungry heroes came to the palace while the king was feasting, and the sight of the banquet increased their hunger, but instead of the fine welcome they had received before, they were now turned away. For Æolus was angry with them for having opened the wind-bag, and, besides, the gods were angry with Ulysses for having ill-treated Polyphemus.

Poor Ulysses and his men turned away and went back to the ships, embarked, and by wind and tide were buffeted about for six days and nights, not knowing whither they went.

To the land of Lamus they were drawn—a land where the people were cannibals. Ulysses, fortunately for himself, did not go into the bay, but remained behind, while some of his comrades rowed right up to the shore and landed, and went reconnoitring.

That was a fatal landing.

The messengers met a fair damsel, who showed them where the king's palace was; they advanced towards it, and presently saw the queen—a hideous woman, who quite scared them. As soon as she set eyes upon the strangers, she called her husband to her, and he, knowing that the men must have come from the sea, gathered many of his giants together and rushed wildly to the shore.

Arrived there, they picked up and hurled huge lumps of rock at the boats riding at anchor in the bay, and killed and made prisoners all the men they could —to the terror and horror of Ulysses.

With his sword the hero slashed at the cables

holding his boat, and called upon his men to pull strongly ; but few of those ill-fated Greeks escaped from the cannibals of Lamus.

4.—THE ISLAND OF CIRCE

THUS reduced in number, and with Fate seeming to dog them wherever they went, the Greeks swept over the seas—anywhere that the wind would carry them ; and after a time they came to an island, where dwelt Circe the sorceress.

Profiting by their mishaps, the heroes now divided into two parties, one under Eurylochus to explore the island, the other to guard the ships against any foes. The island was covered with dense woods, in the centre of which was the palace of Circe. All kinds of animals roamed the forest—but these beasts were tamed by the enchantress and they did not molest the adventurers.

When they came within sight of the palace, the Greeks heard singing—sweet, charming, soothing singing, which lured them on. They were invited by Circe to enter the palace and to stay awhile. Something about this beautiful woman with the lovely voice— perhaps, too, the manner of those beasts who should have been wild, but were meek—aroused the suspicions of Eurylochus, who, of all the band, refused the invitation.

The remainder, going into the palace, found prepared for them a rich feast, to which they began to do justice, for they were famished.

But Circe had drugged the food and wine, which took away from the men all thought of home and friends; and suddenly the sorceress stood up, waved her wand—and the heroes were turned into hogs!

The cruel woman who had inflicted upon these men so dire a calamity—they retained their human senses, and were destined to the filthy existence of the sty—flung them acorns and gloated over their misfortune!

Eurylochus, who had been a startled and astonished onlooker, rushed away to the seashore to tell Ulysses what had happened. His story filled Ulysses with rage; he seized his weapons and told Eurylochus to lead the way, for he vowed he would wreak vengeance upon the inhuman woman who had wrought so great evil.

But Eurylochus implored him not to venture into the enchanted palace, and, despite the commands of Ulysses, refused to accompany him; Ulysses taunted him with cowardice, and left the encampment—alone.

Through the forest he went boldly, smashing his way along, anxious to reach the enchanted palace and to release his men, if that were possible, from the toils of the sorceress.

He had not gone far, however, before he was met by the god Mercury, who appeared to him in human form, and tried to win him from his purpose; but, finding the hero firm in his determination, Mercury gave him an antidote to the drugs which Circe would put in his food and drink.

Mercury told Ulysses that if he ate of the herb, which was called moly, the poison which was placed in his food would have no effect. He told him that as soon as the sorceress lifted her wand to wave it

"Fiercely Frederick bore down upon the unknown knight"

"They hurried after the Piper, laughing and dancing and shouting for joy"

over him, he was to spring to his feet and threaten her with his sword.

Feeling very grateful to Mercury, who then disappeared, Ulysses continued on his way towards the palace, the towers of which glittered in the sunlight. Arrived there, he stood outside the gates, awaiting the pleasure of the evil woman, who presently had her gates swung wide open, came out, and invited the new-comer in.

No fear oppressed the heart of Ulysses, although he knew the dread secret of the palace; the gods had warned him and armed him against Circe's charms.

A glorious feast was spread—wines and rich foods; and every drop and every morsel held the drugs that lulled to forgetfulness and sleep. But, though Ulysses drank deep and ate his fill, yet no film came over his eyes, his head did not droop, nor did his senses grow clouded. Circe, sure in her power to beguile, kept up the feast until she felt the time had come to cast her spell upon this stranger. She arose, a beautiful woman, wand in hand, and the expectant Ulysses saw her wave it as she intoned the words that should have turned the hero into a hog.

But Ulysses still sat on the silver seat to which he had been led—no hog, but a man! Circe stared at him, wondering who this man could be upon whom her drugs, her spells, could have no effect. Ulysses did not give her much time for wondering! He seized his sword, and, whirling it about so that it flashed like leaping flames, he rushed towards her.

Circe shrank from him in terror, crouched at his feet, asked him who he was, wept, pleaded with him.

Ulysses told her his name, and demanded the release of his friends. Circe, who had fallen in love with the hero, promised to set them free, and leading him to a room, in which he was attended by beautiful maidens, went away to the sties where the Greeks grovelled in their animal form.

She swung open the gate, and the herd of hogs who once were men stood before the beautiful woman who had brought them to their sad condition; their grunts made the air hideous—grunts of anger and dismay, as they wondered what fresh evil the sorceress had in store for them. They saw the wand of ill—saw the woman wave it and they scurried to the farthest end of their sties fearful and grunting. But no evil befell them; the waving wand and the chanting of Circe transformed the hogs once more into men!

Never were men so pleased as these who, without hope a moment before, were now delivered from their thraldom; and their joy was increased when, a few moments later, they found themselves reunited to Ulysses, who received them as men back from the dead.

Circe now told Ulysses that he might go back to the shore, run his ships on to the beach, and bring the remainder of his men in safety to the palace. Ulysses, therefore, made his way to where Eurylochus and the rest waited for him; they had, indeed, given up all hope of his ever returning to them, for Eurylochus had told all that he had seen. The sight of their leader, safe and sound, filled them with joy; and when he told them that they might safely follow him to Circe's palace, where everything they wanted awaited them, they clanged their swords and shields, and begged him to lead them forward to the palace of plenty and of pleasure.

All but Eurylochus. He had seen enough of Circe and her spells, and dreaded to go again to the palace. So enraged was Ulysses that he drew his sword and would have struck him, but wiser counsels prevailed.

"Leave him!" he cried. "Leave him here to guard the ship—the man who dares to desert his leader. Come, follow me, you others, to share the glories of Circe's palace."

So the little party started off, but had not gone far before Eurylochus came running after them, having decided to venture into the magic palace.

5.—THE SIRENS' SONG

A WHOLE year did the heroes linger in the land of Circe, taking their ease, finding pleasure in everything, and the sorceress rejoiced that the man she loved stayed with her. But at last the men began to think of Ithaca, and implored their leader to prevail upon Circe to let them go; they knew that if they dared to attempt to leave without permission they would bring her cunning wiles upon them.

The wishes of his men were little different from those of Ulysses himself. He told Circe what was in his heart—how Ithaca called him, and friends he had known were growing to be little more than a memory. Circe tried to dissuade him; used all her harmless arts to keep him by her side, but the longing for home overcame all temptation, and at last she gave them permission to go away.

But, in doing so, she sounded a note of warning.

" You would leave this fair land of mine," she said, " for Ithaca, and I cannot say you nay; but, Ulysses, the gods have many things in store for you before you see your native land again ! "

In wonder, Ulysses asked what the gods had for him, and Circe, with the tongue of a prophetess, told him that he must go to Tiresias, the blind soothsayer, who, in the land of shades, could foretell the things that were going to happen.

The thought of going into the underworld, where lingered the spirits of the men who had died, filled Ulysses with dread ; for one thing he knew not the way thither, for another it must be a fearsome journey.

" You need no mortal guide, Ulysses," said Circe, in answer to his questions. " Run up your mast, set your sail, and the north wind will take you to the ends of the ocean, where you will find yourself in the underworld."

Various other things Circe told the hero, who, realising that the Fates had his life in their hands, prepared for the journey before him, roused his men (one poor fellow, in the excitement of the moment, tumbled headlong from the battlements and was killed), and told them that they were about to leave the land of pleasure.

" Not home to Ithaca is it that we go ! " he cried.

" Whither ? " they demanded eagerly.

" To the underworld — the dreamy realms of darkness and death—there will Tiresias tell us what awaits us."

When the heroes heard what lay before them

they were overwhelmed with grief; they tore their hair, they wept, they entreated the gods to have mercy, flung themselves upon the ground in despair; and yet knew that as the Fates had decreed so must it be.

It was a sad band of men which made its way to the sea shore, where they found the ship still in good condition. They provisioned her, set up her mast, and spread her sail; and then with many a sigh, when night came on, were carried, without needing to ply their oars, at a great speed through the seas until at last they came to the land of gloom. Rocks reared their heads to the mariners, no sun shone there, all was black as night.

And from the blackness came the sound of a river roaring, as it sped on its way to the netherworld, and at this spot, acting according to the instructions of Circe, Ulysses dug a trench, offered sacrifices to the spirits who came crowding round, among them Tiresias, walking by the aid of the staff of gold which the gods had given him when he had been blinded for some fancied ill.

He stooped and drank of the sacrifice, and then prophesied the fate awaiting Ulysses; how that, because of his treatment of Polyphemus, he must suffer many trials before he reached Ithaca—a wanderer on the face of the ocean, doomed to many perilous adventures.

Then, after having met the spirit of his mother, Ulysses, who now realised that his dream of a quiet home-going was not to be, set sail from the land of shadows and returned to Circe's land, where the heroes rested and feasted.

The sorceress, when the time came for Ulysses to depart, told him that the next danger he would meet would come from the cave of the Sirens. She gave advice to the Greeks as to how to protect their leader from the lure of the Sirens' song, which, coming over the sea, had ensnared many a mariner; he who, hearing the music, turned away to discover the singers, was dashed to pieces against the rocks which reared their sharp peaks above the sea.

The heroes boarded their vessel, and for a while a freshening wind carried them along. Then, in the distance, the shores of the Sirens' land appeared like mists, the wind dropped, and the sea fell calm as a mill-pond. Sails were furled, and thrusting out their long sweeps the men pulled strongly.

When the mariners drew nearer to the land, Ulysses took wax which Circe had given him, and melting it in the sun, sealed up the ears of every one of his comrades—for so sure as they heard the song of the Sirens would they go in search of the singers and find their doom. Of all those wandering mariners, Ulysses alone went with unsealed ears, but he commanded his men to bind him to the mast, so that he could not get free. For no wax would keep from his hearing the alluring song of the Sirens.

The long sweeps of the heroes drove the vessel on swiftly towards the now more definite land; the men could hear nothing—but, looking at their leader, they saw him making frantic gestures, as though imploring them to loose him from his bonds.

And well he might! For never did man hear such singing: charming, inviting, soothing—and deceitful. The Sirens called in their songs to Ulysses, whom they knew was passing, invited him to their land, told him that he who listened and followed the music of their voices would be blest; and poor Ulysses was seized with frenzy. He struggled to be free, free that he might go to the sweet singers. He raved at his men, but, safely deaf to the lure and also to the pleadings and threats of Ulysses, the mariners took no heed of his signs; rather, lest he should get free, they added to the number of his bonds.

And Ulysses struggled in vain, while the Sirens sang on and on, increasingly sweetly, as they saw the ship draw nearer. The writhing figure of Ulysses showed them how it was that, instead of making at full speed for shore, the ship was rushing past the place where, sitting on the rocks, the Sirens played upon their lyres and sought to cast their spells over the rowers.

And the ship went by.

Ulysses pleaded with his men to set him free and to turn back. Gently as the dropping of the dew upon petals, the music now fast dying away, fell upon the ears of Ulysses; perhaps because of this it was more alluring than ever, and the hero tore at his bonds. But freedom was not to be his until the last note of the magic music had faded. Then the mariners took the wax from their ears, untied their almost exhausted leader, and prepared for what next might happen.

6.—SCYLLA AND CHARYBDIS

THE men of Ulysses did not know what he knew —that they must pass between the two dread rocks of Scylla and Charybdis, so close together that

263

disaster awaited the ships which sought to make the passage.

For on Scylla was a monster of the same name, who had six mouths and twelve feet—a fearsome beast who barked like a dog; while under Charybdis, opposite, was a whirlpool which three times a day opened its capacious mouth and swallowed the waters of the ocean.

And always near Charybdis the sea was in a turmoil; the waves beat upon the rocks and broke in boiling surf. From Scylla came the barking of the monster—from Charybdis, the roaring of the fiend; altogether it was a scene of terror.

When the heroes came within sight and hearing of the place they were filled with fear; the oars fell from their hands; faces went white. The barking of Scylla seemed to cut into their very brains. The towering rocks seemed to threaten them with disaster; the boiling surf hid, they knew, treacherous points. The whirlpool of Charybdis drew them into its threatening waters, and the yawning gulf appeared to be about to engulf them.

Ulysses, seeing the state of his men, went amongst them seeking to nerve them to attempt the passage; death awaited them all if they did not pull with all their might and seek to keep at a fair distance from the rocks.

" Less danger are we in," he cried, " than when we were locked in the Cyclops' cave; and did not I, your leader, bring you safely out ? "

He told them that he would even this time lead them safely through, ordered them to ply their oars, told the pilot to steer away from the whirlpool, and set his course by the higher rock—Scylla. He carefully refrained from telling them it was Scylla, lest they should take greater fright.

So, when the men, nerved again by their leader's gallant bearing, laboured at the oars, Ulysses, in his shining armour, stood on the prow of the vessel, two gleaming javelins in his hands, on guard, lest the six-mouthed monster should attack them as they swept by the rock.

The channel by Scylla loomed dark and cavernous before him as the ship came full between the two rocks. The noise of the thundering waters, the roaring of Charybdis, the barking of the hideous Scylla, the howling of the wind, all these were deafening and terrifying; but, spurred on by Ulysses, the men toiled at the sweeps, and gradually drawing away from the whirlpool, it seemed that all might yet be well.

But it was not to be. From the yawning black cave, Scylla suddenly swooped and reached out her long neck, and before Ulysses could strike, had seized half a dozen of the mariners. The rest, terror-stricken at the fate of their companions, pulled frantically and swept out of danger before the monster could make a second fell swoop.

As though angry at having missed their prey, Charybdis boomed and Scylla barked; but the vessel had escaped, and coming into calmer waters, sped away towards Trinacria.

7.—ULYSSES AND THE CATTLE OF APOLLO

TRINACRIA was the island of the sun-god Apollo, and the shade of Tiresias had told Ulysses that ere his wanderings were over he would come near this island. There great herds of cattle were reared and kept sacred to the sun-god, whose wrath would descend on the man who dared to kill any of them.

" Do not land on the sun-god's isle," Tiresias had said ; " set your sails before the wind and flee ! "

When Ulysses realised that Trinacria was so near at hand, so near indeed that the grazing herds could be plainly seen, he remembered the words of the seer, and a great fear entered into his heart. For his men were hungry and weary of their labours, battling against stress and storm ; and here were food and rest.

He told them that Tiresias had warned him not to land upon the shore that looked so inviting, but the men were inclined to mutiny at the very thought of passing by a place where seemed to be all they needed most.

" We have followed you," they cried, " through danger and woe, and have fought by your side, have ventured into the land of shadows and barely escaped from the monsters Scylla and Charybdis. Why should we now forgo the rest we need ? "

Ulysses saw the temper of his men's mind, and realised that it would be useless to argue with them. But, before they ran their ship ashore, he warned them against slaughtering any of the sun-god's cattle.

The men vowed that they would obey him in this one thing, at any rate, and joyfully they ran the vessel

The Wanderings of Ulysses

upon the beach and jumped ashore, glad to stretch their cramped and aching limbs.

As though heralding the disaster that was to follow the headstrong conduct of the Greeks in venturing to disregard the warning of Tiresias, hardly had they landed than the sky became clouded, the thunder rolled, a mighty tempest arose, and the earth shook. Even then, however, the Greeks did not flee the island of peace— for such it was to them; they hauled their vessel up on to the shore and prepared for a lengthy stay.

Ulysses, dreading coming events, again warned his men of the danger of killing the sacred beasts, and they promised to beware. For a whole month they tarried on the island, and at the end of that time, their food having given out, they replenished their stores with fish and wild fowl, but at last even these were insufficient to satisfy their hunger. Many were the eager eyes which looked at the herds of cattle roaming free and unmolested through the pasturage; and many a time did a man's hand seek his sword, prompted by the gnawings of hunger, only to fall powerless to his side, as he remembered the warnings of Ulysses.

Food which they could not eat, and a tempestuous sea which they could not venture upon in search of some more hospitable land, such were the tormenting facts that faced the heroes. Ulysses went out and offered a sacrifice to the gods imploring the favour of light winds and calm seas that they might set sail.

And, while he was away, Eurylochus sowed seeds of discontent, which bore fruits of disobedience; the hungering heroes, forgetful of the warning, stole out to the meadows and killed some of the cattle of Apollo.

The prospect of the feast now filled them with joy ; eager hands prepared the food for the cooking, and when Ulysses returned to the camp the smell of the roasting beef came to him.

And he knew in that moment that all was lost. A great fear swept through him as he thought of the vengeance which the sun-god would mete out to those who had dared to slay his cattle.

He hurried into camp, and meantime Lampetia, one of the guardians of the cattle, was hastening to tell the sun-god what had taken place. The gods immediately conferred as to what should be done. Apollo vowed that, unless vengeance was taken on the slayers of his cattle, he would plunge the sun into the ocean ; and this threat was so terrifying that Jupiter promised that the Greeks should be punished ; they should be drowned when they left the island.

Unwitting of the doom awaiting them, the heroes feasted, despite the wrath of Ulysses, who touched none of the food, and in spite also of the signs of a doom from the gods—the food cooking over the fire lowed as if alive ; the empty hides moved along the ground.

Six days the men feasted ; six days the storm raged at sea, as though the gods wished them to fill up the cup of their evil. Then, on the seventh, the sea abated, the wind dropped. Ulysses, anxious to get away hurriedly, made the men embark in the ship— not knowing the fate that awaited the wanderers when once they were at sea.

The calm was deceptive ; it was sent by the gods to lure the heroes to sea. When they were out of sight of land the gale burst out afresh ; huge mountains of sea reared their heads, to fall with a great crash upon the frail craft. The pilot was washed overboard, and Ulysses, seizing the rudder, steered the ship so far as steering was possible in that battle of the elements.

One by one, all those who had partaken of the flesh of the sun-god's cattle were washed overboard and drowned, and only Ulysses remained.

Alone and at the mercy of wind and sea, he held on to the rudder; only to be driven back the way he had come—back to the dread place where Scylla lurked and Charybdis roared.

No effort of Ulysses could keep him from the whirlpool; the roaring waters drew in the vessel whose solitary occupant stood straining at the tiller, as though defying all the elements; round and round the ship swirled, getting nearer and nearer the yawning gulf. No hope there seemed for Ulysses—nothing but a last plunge into the deep blackness.

But the hero had not given up *all* hope ! There was one desperate chance by which he might be saved. At the moment when his boat was about to be sucked in the waters he was near the island of Charybdis, upon which stood a solitary fig tree; with a mighty bound Ulysses sprang ashore, caught the tree, and hung there, and saw his boat drop into the gulf.

Ulysses clung there, helpless; for hours hoping against hope that the whirlpool would disgorge the ship, as it had done many another before. His eager eyes were fixed on the waters; and at last were gladdened by the sight of his vessel—a pitiful wreck of what it was when it set out so proudly from Troy.

But, shattered and leaking though it might be, to

Ulysses it was a barque of salvation; he bided his time, waiting for the moment when it should come near the spot where he was suspended; and then he boldly let go, leaped for the wreck, and, to his great relief, succeeded in jumping aboard.

The waters were now drawing away from Charybdis, and Ulysses seized an oar and pulled frantically, fearing lest he be driven towards Scylla. Fortunately, he escaped, and went bounding over the waters, a lonely wanderer, with memories of disaster behind him, and one hope only in his heart—that some day he would reach Ithaca. For nine days he laboured thus, and at last came to the island of Ogygia, where dwelt a sea-nymph named Calypso, where he remained for no less a time than eight years, because he had no ship in which to sail safely to Ithaca.

8.—ULYSSES' LAST VOYAGE

AWAY in Ithaca, treacherous friends were plotting to destroy his son Telemachus, who had gone to Pylos and Sparta in search of his father. Minerva, the goddess of wisdom, friendly to Ulysses, prevailed at last upon the gods to allow the hero to re-embark for home. Mercury, the winged god, was sent to Calypso, to command her to provide means for Ulysses to leave her island home. Calypso was angry, but the will of the gods could not be gainsaid; she could not keep the hero who for long weary years had been thinking of, and sighing for, Ithaca.

She told Ulysses what the gods had decreed, and

270

bade him fell trees in the forest and build himself a
raft. But the hero, who had met so many perilous adventures while sailing in strong ships, and with men
at his beck and call, thought that Calypso was taunting him.

"How can a man trust himself to a raft in so vast
an ocean?" he cried. "Some evil towards me is in
your mind!"

Calypso assured him of her honest intentions, and the
hero, with a new hope in his heart, set to work to build
the raft, and, aided by the sea-nymph, in due course had
ready a vessel of a kind—half raft, half boat, with a
sail woven by Calypso.

Food and drink were put on board, and then
the lonely wanderer, bidding farewell to the nymph,
launched his craft, pushed off, and was bounding over
the seas, free once more to seek his home and friends.

But his troubles were not yet over. Neptune, who
had been angered by the punishment Ulysses had
inflicted upon Polyphemus, suddenly discovered that
the hero might escape back to Ithaca. Determined to
do all he could to prevent him, he raised terrible storms,
which tossed the frail barque about in such an alarming
manner that Ulysses almost gave up in despair.

There was little time for despair, however; a great
wave lifted the craft high, dropped it with a resounding
crash, and Ulysses was struggling in the waters for his life.

By good luck he succeeded in regaining the raft;
and the fight with the storm went on until Leucothea,
the sea-nymph, came to his rescue.

"Strip and plunge into the waves," she called out
to him, "and put on this scarf."

Ulysses, amazed at the coming of the nymph, was willing to take every chance of life, yet when the goddess disappeared, for a moment or so he stood in hesitation, wondering whether this might not be a trap set by Neptune.

"I will remain on the raft," he said to himself. "That at least is safe!"

But the raft was not safe.

A mighty wave overwhelmed it and shattered it to pieces, and left Ulysses clinging to a piece of wreckage. The catastrophe resolved his doubts for him; he quickly divested himself of his clothes, put on the magic scarf that Leucothea had given him, and plunged into the sea.

While he was swimming, Neptune appeared, riding on his sea-green horses. The god was angry; he could see himself being robbed of the victim of his rage. Yet he knew that he could not prevail against the decrees of the gods, and told Ulysses to go on his way.

"But know," he said, "that all the ills of my anger shall remain with you always!"

Glad to be rid of the trident-bearing adversary, Ulysses swam on, and after three days, during which he was held up safely by the magic scarf, he came to the land of Phæacia, where he made his way ashore, and, exhausted, flung himself down to sleep in the forest, having first, as commanded by Leucothea, hurled the scarf back into the sea.

While Ulysses slept, Minerva hastened to the court of Alcinous, the king of Phæacia, and there she told his daughter Nausicaa to go down to the sea to wash her state robes, ready for her wedding day, and the happy princess, gathering her servants around her, went down to the shore. Arrived there, they washed the clothes, and then began a game of ball.

Near where they played, Ulysses slept the sleep of exhaustion; but one of the maidens flung the ball far out into the water, and, to accompanying shrieks of laughter, she swam for it.

The noise of their mirth awakened the hero, who, wondering what it meant, and thinking that he had fallen upon a hostile shore, leapt to his feet and rushed out of the forest, breaking down a tree to make himself a covering of leaves.

And, to his great relief, he found no enemies, but sportive maidens, who fled in terror from the strange figure who came out of the woods. Alone of them all the princess remained to welcome the hero, who did not tell her who he was, except that he was an unfortunate wanderer needing succour. Nausicaa recalled her maidens, bade Ulysses welcome to the land, and after providing him with clothes, told him to go up to the palace.

Nausicaa went up before him, and while the hero was threading his way along he met a beautiful maiden (no other, although he knew it not, than Minerva). She showed him, at his request, the road to the palace, and told him how to approach the king; and when Ulysses, whom Minerva had cloaked about by a veil of invisibility, arrived at the palace, he was amazed at the splendour of it. The like he had never seen before; its brazen walls gleamed in the sun; its doors were of gold, its pillars of silver; and everything about it rich beyond imagination.

Yet, boldly, Ulysses went in and threw himself at the feet of the queen, and the mist of invisibility was dispersed. He paid homage, and after a little delay found himself seated at the side of the king's son, Laodamas, feasting with the gay company. He quickly made friends, and next day, when the games were held, he entered the arena against the best players in Phæacia, and challenged them, one and all; and the king was astonished at his prowess. After the sports, high honour was paid to him at the feast that was held.

The king's minstrel came to that feast, and sang of the story of Troy; which, when he heard it, with all its memories of evil days and good, caused Ulysses to weep. So great was his emotion that the king commanded to know who he was that the recital of the story should move him to tears and cause such evident despair.

Ulysses at last composed himself sufficiently to tell of his adventures since the day he set sail from Troy, and when he had finished the king and his courtiers were moved with compassion.

Alcinous promised to give him all the assistance he could to enable him to reach Ithaca; fitted out a vessel with treasures, and provided a crew, who, after Ulysses had bidden farewell to his friends, bent to the oars and ploughed the seas—Minerva watching over the hero and preventing Neptune from impeding his safe progress.

At last the fair shores of Ithaca came into view; but Ulysses saw them not, for he was lying asleep in the ship.

The sailors ran their vessel ashore, and after empty-

ing it of its riches, they bore Ulysses to land. He was
still asleep on his couch, and they left him there and set
out for their own land. But Neptune, who now realised
that he was robbed of the victim of his anger, took
vengeance on the men of King Alcinous for having
carried Ulysses to his country; and wrecked their
ship against a great rock which barred the harbour
of Phæacia.

9.—PLOTTINGS AT ITHACA

MEANWHILE in Ithaca Ulysses awoke from his sleep,
and yet knew not that he was in his own country,
for Minerva, in order to shield him from foes, had
enveloped him again in the mist of invisibility.

While he was wondering what more ills might befall
him—for he remembered nothing but that before he
slept he was on the ship—Minerva appeared before him
and told where he was. She told him to hide his
treasures, disguise himself as a beggar, and make his
way inland, where he could learn how things stood at
the court of Ithaca.

She touched him with her magic wand; his skin
became shrivelled, he stooped, his hair was white as
an old man's, and not one of his friends would have
known him.

Thus disguised, Ulysses found his way to the house
of Eumaeus, once his swineherd. He kept up the fiction
of being an old beggar, and entering into conversation,
found that most of the people of Ithaca believed
that Ulysses was dead. A number of suitors were

275

pressing his wife, Penelope, to choose a second husband. She, however, refused to do so; and her son, Telemachus, had gone in quest of his father, who he believed still lived. The young prince, however, at the urging of Minerva, set out to return home, and the suitors, hearing that he was coming, laid an ambush for him; but Telemachus passed safely through and landed in Ithaca, just near the place where his father was sheltered by Eumaeus.

Then Telemachus went up to the house of the swineherd, and commanded him to hasten to court and acquaint Penelope of his return. While the servant had gone, Ulysses and Telemachus, who did not know his father, met and conversed, and Minerva, having thus brought them together, appeared to Ulysses, waved over him her magic wand, and the old beggar, weak and bent, was transformed into the hero.

He stood before Telemachus, who looked at him with astonishment, and was more amazed than ever when the stranger cried:

" I am your father ! "

The meeting between father and son was affectionate, for Telemachus had longed to find Ulysses, if only to bring him back to Penelope, who mourned him as one dead.

After the first transports of joy, Telemachus told his father of the suitors who sought to press Penelope to another marriage, and the father and son planned how to foil the plotters.

Telemachus was to go back to the court and tell no one of the return of Ulysses, who would go up to the palace disguised as a beggar and crave hospitality.

The Wanderings of Ulysses

10.—THE RETURN OF ULYSSES

So, scarcely able to tear himself away from his father's side, the young prince went to the palace, and a little later the beggar-man arrived and received admission.

None but his old dog Argus, a faithful hound, recognised the returned king, and so overjoyed was he that he fell dead at his feet.

The poor beggar was admitted to the presence of Penelope, who questioned him lest he should have any news of her husband. So effective was his disguise that she did not recognise him as the man she loved and longed to see once more.

Poor Penelope was growing tired of the pleadings of the suitors. For years she had put them off for one reason or another, and she had told them that she would not make her choice until she had finished a piece of tapestry on which she was engaged. For three years she seemed to make little progress, until at last the princes discovered that every night she undid what she had done during the day !

They were very angry, and told her that she must finish the work ; and poor Penelope, anxious to gain as much time as she could, in the hope that some news might be heard of her husband, had to devise some other method by which she could put off the evil day on which she must make the fateful decision pressed for by her powerful suitors.

The suitors were by no means friendly towards Telemachus, whom they even sought to kill, to the grief of Penelope. Antinous, one of the Greeks who seemed the most friendly, was in reality the most treacherous, and altogether Penelope and Telemachus were surrounded by foes.

The heart of Ulysses was very troubled as he saw and heard all that Penelope had to put up with; yet he dared not declare himself until the right moment arrived. These foes must be met by cunning; and Ulysses abided his time. After various adventures, in one of which he defeated Irus, a giant and a beggar who lived on the bounty of the court, and resented the coming of this new beggar, as he regarded Ulysses, the latter, still unrecognised by Penelope, found an opportunity to get rid of the suitors for her hand.

He had told Penelope a story of her husband, who, he said, he had known, and assured the queen that the hero still lived. Penelope was now more than ever desirous of putting off the day of choice, and at a feast which was held she proclaimed a new condition, one which she knew would be hard to fulfil.

"To the man who can bend Ulysses' bow," she said, "and drive the arrow through twelve rings—to that man will I give myself!"

It was a wonderful bow, and most of the suitors knew how difficult a task was set them, and they would have refused had not Telemachus insisted; the young prince himself was to compete—his prize, if victorious, to be his mother's freedom.

So at last the contest began.

Telemachus first took the bow, fitted an arrow into it, and tried three times to twang the bow—and failed. His strength was not equal to the task.

The Wanderings of Ulysses

At the fourth time, however, he pulled it, and would have sent the arrow winging towards the twelve rings, had not Ulysses by a sign forbidden him to do so.

Telemachus, knowing that his father did not want the suitors to imagine it was a planned affair, threw the bow aside, asserting that he was not strong enough, for Ulysses had seen in this contest a chance to get the better of his foes.

Then, one after another, but all in vain, the suitors took up the mighty bow; and when all of them except Antinous and Eurymachus had tried, Antinous soaked the weapon in grease; he was determined by some means or other to bend the bow and win the queen for wife.

While this was being done, Ulysses went out to the swineherds and revealed himself to them; and they were overjoyed to have their chief back again. After the heartfelt greetings were over, Ulysses told them of his plan; they were all to go into the hall where the combat was to be settled, taking care to see that all the doors were bolted. Ulysses himself was to go in and Eumaeus was to place the bow in the hands of his master if the suitors would not allow him to have it by fair means, which he intended to try.

Into the great hall the faithful swineherds trooped, and after them the insignificant beggar, whom the suitors despised, but whom Penelope befriended because he had given her news of Ulysses.

A strange sight met the eyes of Ulysses. His bow, which had laid many an enemy low in the days before his departure for Troy, the bow that no man but he himself could bend, was being held over a great fire, and a man was rubbing it with grease to make it supple.

279

Eurymachus was fuming because this was necessary.

" How shameful a thing it is that we must own ourselves weaker than Ulysses ! "

But Antinous would not have it so. He found an excuse in the fact that that day was sacred to Phœbus ; he was a crafty man, and had been content that the other suitors should test their strength when all the time he believed the god was against them for doing so, while he was determined to try his own prowess on a more auspicious day !

His suggestion that he and Eurymachus should wait until the morrow was agreed to, and the warriors prepared to spend the day in feasting ; but Ulysses, the stranger whom they hated, rose, and facing them, said :

" Since you will wait until to-morrow, I, an old man whose only consolation is the memory of his past strength, beg to hold for one moment the bow of Ulysses. Fain would I see if my arm has lost its power ! "

When he had finished Antinous jumped to his feet, and in a rage poured scorn upon the poor man, and vowed that if he succeeded in bending the bow he should be cast adrift upon the ocean. Eurymachus also begged that the stranger should not be allowed to test his strength, lest, aided by the gods, he should be able to bend the bow, and the names of noble warriors go down to posterity with the stigma upon them that an old man did what they could not.

There was a wordy quarrel, and while it was proceeding, Eumaeus, true to his promise, took the bow to Ulysses, who, knowing that all the doors were locked, drew the bow, while the suitors looked ; and to their

The Wanderings of Ulysses

terror he drew it full out, the arrow slipped from the string and sped like lightning through the air, through every one of the twelve rings, through even the stout gates of the palace !

Instantly all was confusion. The suitors drew their swords; Telemachus, at a sign from his father, who, he knew, was now about to deal with the plotters, took up his stand at the old man's side; and almost at once another arrow sped, this time on an errand of death. Antinous fell to the ground, dead.

Then, revealing his identity to the rest of the suitors, Ulysses found himself face to face with all his foes; there was a terrific fight, out of which Ulysses and his son, aided by Minerva, who appeared disguised as Mentor, came victorious.

And when the fight was over, a servant rushed to tell Penelope the news of the return of Ulysses. The poor queen could scarcely believe what she heard, and although Ulysses came later on and told her his story, she would not believe that he was indeed her long-lost husband until he had proved his identity by telling her a secret which only they two in all the world knew.

For thirty years, during which he had been fighting, adventuring, wandering, Ulysses had been absent from Ithaca; and he had even now to fight against his neighbours, while his subjects rebelled. In these wars Ulysses was victorious, and afterwards settled down with Penelope to reign over his kingdom.

The Story of Sir Galahad

SIR GALAHAD was the youngest of all King Arthur's knights. He had been brought up in an abbey by the abbess and her nuns, and when he was old enough Sir Lancelot knighted him and took him to King Arthur's court. He was brave and fearless, and strong with the strength that comes from pureness of heart.

> "My strength is as the strength of ten
> Because my heart is pure."

On the very day that he first came to Camelot a wonderful thing happened. A great stone floated down the river with a sword fast wedged in it. The sword was of beautiful workmanship, and the hilt was encrusted with many rare and precious stones, and on it was an inscription, "Never shall man take me hence but he by whose side I ought to hang, and he shall be the best knight in the world."

Then all the knights of King Arthur's court tried to pull the sword from the stone, but there was not one of them who could move it.

But when Sir Galahad arrived at Camelot and heard of the wonderful sword he stepped down to the river side and laid his hand upon the hilt. And he drew the sword from the stone as easily as though it were but from his scabbard.

The Story of Sir Galahad

The other knights were amazed that a youth who
was scarcely more than a boy should be able to draw
the sword when so many older and stronger men had
failed in doing so, and they looked at him in wonder.
" Surely he is destined for some great quest," they
whispered amongst themselves, and after that, although
they were always kind and gentle to Sir Galahad, they
treated him with reverence and awe, as one marked out
for some great achievement.

Not very long after Galahad had come to Arthur's
court the king and his knights were sitting one day
at table, when suddenly everything grew dark around
them. A great crash of thunder was heard, and then
a beam of dazzling light shot into the hall where they
were sitting. And down the beam of light came gliding
the Holy Grail, the cup from which our Saviour drank
at the Last Supper. It was covered with a white cloth
so that no man might see it, and when it had travelled
the length of the hall it disappeared from sight.

For a few moments there was silence in the great
hall, then Sir Gawaine sprang to his feet with a sudden
impulse.

" I make a vow," he cried, " that to-morrow I will
set out in the quest of the Holy Grail, and never more
will I return to this court until I have seen the sacred
cup itself."

Then all the other knights arose to their feet and
made the same vow, and Arthur's heart sank within
him. He knew that his company of brave knights
was now broken up for ever, and he wondered sadly
how many of those who set out on this great quest
would be worthy to achieve it.

The next day all the knights who had taken the vow rode forth from the castle, and so started the quest for the Holy Grail. The king's presentiment came sadly true, for only two or three of all that brave company were destined to catch even a fleeting glimpse of the sacred vessel. There was only one who was worthy to look upon it. All the others were stained with sin, and none but the pure in heart were fit to receive the full vision of the Holy Grail. The one who did succeed in the quest was Sir Galahad, the boy knight of the Round Table. And even he, pure and stainless as he was, had to pass through many dangers and much suffering before he was permitted to see the vision.

After he had parted from the other knights Galahad rode for several days without meeting with any adventure. He was armed with the sword he had drawn from the stone on the first day he came to Camelot, but as yet he had no shield.

One evening, with two other knights, he took shelter at an abbey where a wonderful silver shield was kept. This shield was said to bring death and disaster to all who were bold enough to wear it, save only to him for whom it was intended.

One of the knights declared his intention of arming himself with this shield. In spite of the abbot's warning, he took it down from its place behind the altar, and set off with it on his arm, attended by his squire. But he had hardly gone any distance at all when a strange knight rode down upon him, bore him from his horse, and took the shield away.

"None may bear this shield save only he who hath no peer in this world," the strange knight said. Then

284

he turned to the squire, saying, "Carry this shield to Sir Galahad, he alone is worthy to bear it," and the frightened squire at once obeyed him.

And so Sir Galahad, armed with the magic sword and shield, rode forth from the abbey to do battle for the right, and to search for the vision of the Holy Grail. So great was the power of his sword that, young as he was, no man could stand against him, and the wonderful shield saved him from any bodily harm. Once, as he knelt at prayer, he heard a voice telling him to ride to the castle of seven wicked brothers and set free the captives he found there. Sir Galahad obeyed at once, and though he was only one against seven, yet the strength of his sword and the protecting power of his shield were such that he overcame and conquered them all, and set the poor captives free.

He journeyed through many lands, meeting with many strange adventures, and always he did battle for the weak, and righted wrongs whenever he came across them. And yet through all his trials and difficulties and adventures he kept his heart as pure and stainless as it was when he first left the abbey and ventured out into the world.

At length he fell, with two other knights, into the hands of a pagan king, who treated his captives very cruelly and shut them up in prison. The king would have starved Sir Galahad and his two companions; but for a whole year they were fed by the Holy Grail, which appeared in their prison every day. But yet they never actually saw the sacred cup, for always it was covered with a white cloth.

After they had spent a whole year in prison the wicked

king fell ill, and when he knew he was dying he sent for the three knights and begged their forgiveness. And after he was dead his counsellors chose Galahad to be their king.

So for some time Sir Galahad stayed in that country and ruled over the people wisely and well, and the two knights who had been his companions in captivity stayed with him.

One day, as he knelt with his friends at prayer before the altar, a holy man appeared before the young king.

" Galahad, thou servant of Christ," he said, " now shalt thou see clearly that which thou hast so long desired. I am Joseph of Arimathea, and I am come to show you the perfect vision of the Holy Grail."

The chapel was filled with radiant light, and the holy vessel appeared without its covering. The two companions of Sir Galahad had one moment's vision of the sacred cup, but the light was too dazzling for their eyes, and they were obliged to turn away. Only Galahad could gaze steadfastly at the vision, and he alone saw the perfect beauty of the Holy Grail.

And as he gazed a multitude of angels thronged around him, and his pure soul was lifted in their hands and carried into heaven.

When the two knights were able to look to the altar again the light and the vision had vanished. Sir Galahad was still kneeling before the altar in an attitude of prayer, but when they rose and went to him they found that he was dead.

And after Sir Galahad no man ever saw the vision of the Holy Grail.

The Passing of Arthur

AND now the end was coming to King Arthur's glorious reign. The quest of the Holy Grail had broken up the fellowship of the Round Table, and the knights were scattered far and wide. Many of them had died in foreign lands, and when once again the hordes of savage tribes invaded the realm there were few of them left to fight beside the king.

Arthur knew that the end had come, but yet, dauntless as ever, he gathered together the remnant of his followers and marched out to meet the enemy.

Bravely he and his knights fought as of old, but the old trust and confidence in victory was gone, and then, in the midst of their hard struggle, a fresh blow came to dishearten them.

One of the knights of the Round Table, the king's own nephew, a man named Modred, turned traitor, and joined the forces of the heathen tribes to fight against the king. And some of the people who had never believed that Arthur was the rightful king flocked to his standard, so that before long there was a formidable army arrayed against the king.

For a long time the issue of the war was still in doubt, and then came the last great battle amongst the mountains of Wales—the last battle that the great king was ever to fight.

All day long the battle raged, until at length of all the brave knights on either side there were none left save only the king and Sir Bedivere.

Worst of all the king was wounded, so seriously that Sir Bedivere feared that he would die. Bedivere lifted the wounded king in his arms and carried him from that ghastly battlefield to a little chapel that stood beside a lake not far away. There he laid him on the stone floor and took off his helmet, and did his best to bring him back to life.

But Arthur knew that his end had come. He knew that his reign was over, that his brave company of knights was broken up for ever, and that it would be many, many years before peace came back to the land he loved so dearly.

He drew his sword from its sheath, and gave it to Sir Bedivere, and told him to take it to the edge of the lake and fling it far out into the water.

Now his sword, which was called Excalibur, was a very wonderful sword, and had a strange history. It had never been made by man, and no man could stand when it was wielded against him.

Long ago, when Arthur was in need of a sword, Merlin, the wise man who had brought the king up and taken care of him when he was a child, had brought him to the edge of this very lake, and there, in the middle of the lake, a white arm was stretched out of the water holding the sword in its hand. Arthur had rowed across the water and taken the sword, and the arm had immediately disappeared below the surface.

Excalibur was a very beautiful sword, the hilt was encrusted with diamonds and topaz and jacinth and

288

The Passing of Arthur

amethyst and other rare gems. On one side of the
blade was written " Keep me," and on the other " Throw
me away." Carefully had Arthur kept the precious
talisman through his life, and now he knew that the time
was come for him to throw it away.

Sir Bedivere took the sword and left the little chapel,
and when he reached the edge of the lake, he drew the
sword to cast it away. But when he saw the jewels and
the splendid workmanship of the hilt, his heart failed
him. It seemed wrong to throw such a marvellous
sword into the water.

" The king is sick," he said to himself. " He knows
not what he does. If he were in his right mind he would
not tell me to do such a thing." And hiding the sword
amongst the rushes, he went back to the little chapel.

The king was anxiously awaiting him.

" What did you see ? " he cried. And Sir Bedivere
answered :

" Naught, oh king. The lake was still and quiet.
I saw and heard nothing but the ripple washing in the
reeds."

Arthur looked at his knight in anger and disappoint-
ment.

" You have betrayed me," he said. " That is not
a true answer, for a surer sign had followed had you
done as I commanded. Go quickly now, and do the
thing I bade you, and come and bring me word again."

Sir Bedivere went a second time to the water's edge,
but when again he saw the wonder of the hilt, he smote
his hands together and cried aloud :

" How can I do this thing that my lord commands
me ? Surely such a precious record of the king should

not be cast away." And once again he hid the sword and went back to Arthur.

Arthur looked up at him eagerly as he drew near.

" What have you seen, or what have you heard ? " he said.

Then Bedivere answered again :

" I heard the water lapping on the crag, and the long ripple washing in the reeds."

The king raised himself painfully on his elbow and spoke angrily to Sir Bedivere.

" Oh, you have played me false ! " he cried. " You are untrue, unknightly. You would betray me for the sake of the precious stones in the hilt. Once more will I send you, and if you fail in my behest this time, dying though I am, I will arise and slay you with my own hands."

Then Sir Bedivere ran quickly to the lake, and seizing the sword he swung it round his head and flung it far from him over the water. But before it touched the surface a white arm shot out of the lake and caught it by the hilt. Three times the hand waved the blade in the air, and then drew it under the water.

Sir Bedivere went back to the little chapel, and King Arthur saw by the look in his face that this time he had done what was commanded.

" Speak," he said. " What have you seen or heard ? "

And then Sir Bedivere told him how he had flung the sword Excalibur out over the lake and how an arm had come up out of the water and caught the hilt, and having waved the blade three times in the air had disappeared below the water.

The Passing of Arthur

Then Arthur breathed a deep sigh.

" My end is nigh," he said. " It is time that I were gone. Carry me now to the water side."

Sir Bedivere lifted the dying king tenderly in his arms and bore him out of the little ruined chapel down to the margin of the lake. And as they reached it a long black barge, filled with black-robed figures, came gliding towards them over the water. Three queens, wearing crowns of gold, were seated in the barge, and as they drew near to land they reached out their hands and lifted the dying king from the arms of his knight and laid him gently down upon the deck, wailing and sighing as they did so. Then the barge, moving as mysteriously as it came, began to glide away.

When Sir Bedivere saw that his king and master was being borne away from him, he cried out and begged him not to go and leave him desolate in a strange, sorrowful world.

" Whither shall I go ? " he cried. " Where shall I hide my eyes, for now, indeed, I see the old true times are dead ! "

Then Arthur answered slowly and faintly from the barge :

" You cannot come with me now, for I am going a long way to the island valley of Avalon, where neither snow nor rain ever falls, and where I shall heal me of my grievous wound. And if you should never see my face again—pray for my soul."

Then the barge moved slowly away, and Sir Bedivere, standing beside the lake, watched it growing fainter and fainter in the distance until at last it disappeared from sight, and the cries of the black-robed figures died away.

That was the end of Arthur's kingdom. Sir Bedivere and Lancelot, and the few remaining knights of the Round Table, entered a hermitage and became good and holy men, withdrawing themselves from the world and giving their lives to prayer. Queen Guinevere, too, went into a convent, and lived a pure and holy life for many years.

And as for Arthur, he whose reign had been so great and glorious, and who had lived such a true upright life, no man knew for certain what became of him. Some people said that he had died and was buried, but others said that he still lived in the valley of Avalon, and would one day come again into the world and reign over the people of England. And in the West of England people still believe that somewhere Arthur lies sleeping, waiting for the day to dawn when he shall once more come forth to his country's aid, to help her in her hour of greatest need.

The Legend Beautiful

A MONK was once kneeling in his cell, praying.
He was a good man, and he lived a holy and
pure life. Every day for long hours he knelt
alone in his little narrow room in the convent, lifting
up his heart in prayer to God, asking for forgiveness
for his human failings, offering thanks and praise for
the many blessings vouchsafed to him, and praying
for strength to resist the temptations that came in
his way.

As he knelt there, on the cold stones of the floor,
a sudden bright light filled the dark, bare room, and
lifting up his eyes, the monk saw the Christ to whom
he was praying so earnestly standing there before him
in the narrow cell, robed in splendour and shining
with the glory and radiance of Paradise.

In his exaltation and wonder the monk could
not utter a word. He could only gaze in awe and love
and reverence at his gracious visitor. Surely he was
blessed among men for his Lord to deign to enter
his poor humble cell, and show Himself in all His
loveliness to His servant's dazzled eyes!

He knelt on, still gazing speechlessly at the vision,
scarcely daring to breathe for fear the shining figure
should vanish, content to remain for ever looking on
the wonderful sight. But suddenly a familiar sound

broke through the rapture of that moment. The convent bell began to ring loudly and insistently, calling the poor, the lame and the blind to the convent gate to receive the daily portion of bread and wine which the good brothers distributed amongst them through summer and winter alike. And the monk remembered with a pang of horror and dismay that it was his duty to go to the gate and dole out the alms.

But how could he go ? Surely when the dear Lord Christ Himself came and with His glorious presence graced the little convent cell, surely he could not go away and leave Him ? Would it not be slighting his heavenly guest to desert Him for a crowd of poor ragged beggars ? Surely the right thing to do was to remain in his attitude of humble adoration and taste to the full the glory and exaltation of this wonderful hour ?

But then came the thought of the poor people gathered outside the gate. They could wait. Yes, but many of them were old and feeble, hungry and sick. The food the brothers gave them was all that many of them tasted from one day to another. They could wait, but there was so much of waiting in their poor sad lives—was it right to add to that waiting one hour or one moment more than was necessary ?

In deep distress and uncertainty, the monk lingered —should he go or stay ? In his perplexity, torn between his devotion to his duty and his adoration of his Master, he tried to think what that Master would have done had He been in his place. Would the Man who had walked amongst the fields of Galilee, who had healed the sick and cleansed the lepers, who had been the friend of the halt and maimed, the poor, the sick, and the blind—would He have left His brothers and sisters to wait in cold and hunger outside the convent gate? As he asked himself the question, the monk saw what he must do.

"Do thou thy duty; leave the rest to God," whispered a voice in his heart; and rising to his feet the monk took one last look at the shining figure. and left his cell.

Surely there were more beggars than usual that day? It seemed to the monk that he would never finish doling out the bread and wine—that he would never be able to get back to his own little room and meditate in solitude and silence upon the vision which had been vouchsafed to him. Had he perhaps done wrong, after all, to go away and leave his Lord? Ought he, after all, to have stayed? Oh, that his duty at the gate were over so that he could have leisure to examine himself and decide whether he had done right or wrong!

At length that long hour came to an end. The last beggar had turned away, calling down blessings from Heaven upon the good brothers who had befriended him, the iron gates shut to with a clang, and the monk was free at last to go back to his cell. As he turned his face towards the convent it seemed to him to be lighted up with a ray of supernatural glory that turned the grey walls to gold. A sudden wonderful hope flashed into the monk's mind, and with beating heart he hurried back towards his lonely room.

Famous Myths and Legends

Eagerly he passed down the long corridor leading to it, eagerly he flung back the door; then he stopped short on the threshold with a heart so full of love and joy and wonder that he scarcely knew how to control his feelings.

For his cell was still filled with heavenly radiance, the glorious figure of his Lord stood there still.

Trembling with happiness, the monk sank upon his knees, holding out his hands in worship towards that radiant figure, and even as he did so the vision spoke :

"Hadst thou stayed, I must have fled," it said, and the monk's heart burned within him as at last he understood all that his Lord would have him learn. The pure, holy life he led was good, but it was not enough. Fasting and prayer and solitude and self-denial, essential though they might be, were no use by themselves. The only way for mortal man to find and keep the vision of the perfect life was through his work and love and service for mankind.

St. Patrick

MORE than fourteen hundred years ago there lived in Ireland a little slave boy. He had been carried away from his home by the wild Irish raiders, and had been given to a rich man for a slave.

Patrick—for that was the boy's name—was put to minding the sheep amongst the wild brown bogs in the north of Ireland. It was hard, rough work, and often the weather was cold and wet and windy; sometimes even, in the winter, thick snow lay upon the ground. But Patrick's master cared nothing for the sufferings of his herd-boy; and whatever the weather was, Patrick was obliged to be out in it, tending his sheep. It was a lonely, solitary life he led, and the boy, who had been brought up as a Christian, began to think a great deal of his early teaching. Perhaps, too, being always amongst the wild life of the country brought him nearer to God than many boys of his age. However that may have been, he did begin to think a great deal about his religion, and soon all his time that was not passed in work was spent in offering prayers and thanks and praises to his heavenly Father.

One night, when he had been a captive for six years, he heard in a dream a voice saying to him :

" Behold, a ship is ready for thee—thou shalt return to thy country!" And believing it to be the voice of God, Patrick took the first opportunity to escape from his master.

He wandered on for a great way until he reached the coast, and there, sure enough, was a ship just about to leave the country. Patrick begged the master of the ship to take him with him, but the master at first would not do so. Then Patrick went away and prayed to God, and while he was still praying he heard one of the men calling for him.

" Come along—the master is asking for thee," he said. And when Patrick reached the ship again, he found that the master had decided to take him with them, after all.

So Patrick came once more to his native land. When they left the boat the little company of sailors had still many miles to walk before they could reach a town, and the country was wild and desolate. They had not many provisions, and at one time it seemed as though they would perish with hunger. Then the men turned to the young man they had brought with them from Ireland.

" Christian! Your God is powerful. Pray for us, for we are starving with hunger!" they said.

Then Patrick made the men all kneel down, and he knelt too and prayed with them; and suddenly, as they were praying, a drove of swine came by. The men rushed after them and killed and captured many of them. Then they gave great thanks to the God of Patrick, and so St. Patrick made his first converts.

St. Patrick

Patrick reached his home at last, but he did not remain there for many years. For one night, in his sleep, he had another dream which he thought came to him from God, and was sent to call him back to the country of his captivity. He dreamt that he saw a man coming towards him holding a letter which, when he had opened it, proved to have come from the Irish people, and at the same time he thought he heard a cry from many voices saying:

"Come, holy boy! Come and walk still in the midst of us!"

After this dream Patrick made up his mind to go again to Ireland and endeavour to convert the Irish people to the worship of the true God. In time he was ordained a priest, and then, with a few chosen companions, he set off on his holy mission.

He had uphill work at first, but his zeal and energy overcame all obstacles. Gradually the people came to love and reverence the holy man who, by the power of his prayer, was able to perform so many miracles; and at length they learned to love and reverence too the God of whom he spoke.

Before St. Patrick brought Christianity to Ireland, the country was overrun with snakes and other venomous reptiles. There were so many of them that they became quite a plague in the land, and they did a great deal of harm and killed a great number of people. But one day St. Patrick, who had often prayed to God about the plague of snakes that troubled Ireland, went to the top of a high mountain, carrying in his hand the staff which showed that he was a priest. Then, by the power of his prayer and faith, he charmed

299

the snakes until he had every one of them collected before him, and drove them all into the sea.

The people could scarcely believe their eyes when they saw this miracle, and as they gathered eagerly round the saint to hear his words, St. Patrick began to tell them again of the love and power of God. He told them about the Father who had made the world, of the Son who had died in order to save men from their sins, of the Holy Ghost who came to guide and direct men's hearts and minds, and he tried to explain to them that though these were three persons, yet were they not three Gods but one God.

But the peasant people, uneducated and ignorant as they were, could not understand him, and St. Patrick was in despair as to how he was to explain his meaning, when suddenly, looking down, he saw a little green three-leafed plant growing at his feet.

"See," he cried, plucking a spray of it and holding it up before the people. "Here are three leaves, yet they form but one leaf. So are there three Gods, yet they are but one God." And the people, seeing the little green plant, began to understand St. Patrick's meaning.

So St. Patrick lived and worked amongst the Irish people and did so much good that after his death he became the patron saint of Ireland, and the little green plant, the shamrock, which he had used to explain the great doctrine of the Trinity, was made the national emblem. The story about his charming the snakes is, of course, only a legend, yet still to this very day there are no snakes in Ireland.

The Legend of the Cuckoo

ONCE upon a time, a very long while ago, there lived a baker. He had a big business, and as he was very industrious and worked hard he soon began to grow rich. Some of his customers were wealthy folks, and for them the baker made the dough and baked the loaves and sent them round to their houses. But the greater part were poor people, who could not afford to buy their bread in this way. So they mixed the flour and water themselves, and then brought the dough to the baker to be baked in his oven.

But the baker was so anxious to grow rich that he began to forget to be honest, and when the poor people brought him their loaves to be baked, he used to break off some of the dough before he put the loaves into the oven. And when the people came with their money to fetch the bread, he would bring out the loaves, saying with a shake of his head :

"Look how they have shrunk in the baking! You have made them of inferior flour, good people."

This went on for a long time, until at last there was a famine in the land, and bread became very dear indeed. Yet still the baker stole the dough from the loaves of the poor people, and when they complained at the shrinkage in their bread he would say with a laugh :

" Look, look, what did I tell you ? You have made them of inferior flour, good people." And though the people knew that there must be something wrong, they could not take their loaves elsewhere to be baked, for there was no other baker in the town.

But such dishonesty was not to be allowed to go on for ever. One day, when the people came as usual to the bakehouse, they found instead of a baker a little brown bird, who flew away over the housetops calling, " Cuckoo, cuckoo—look, look."

It was the baker. He had been changed into a cuckoo because of his dishonest ways, and now he flies about the world in the guise of a little brown bird, with a dirty, ash-coloured look about him as though he were sprinkled with flour, as a punishment for having stolen the bread of the poor people.

And everywhere he goes he calls " Cuckoo—look, look," as he used to do so long ago when he showed his poor customers their shrunken loaves.

Diarmid and Grania

WHEN Finn the Irish hero was growing an old man, he became very lonely, for his wife was dead and his children were grown up. He began to think he would take another wife, so he sent Oisin his son and another of his men to the high king of Ireland to ask for the hand of his daughter Grania in marriage.

Now Grania was a beautiful woman, and many were the men who had wanted to marry her; but she was proud and haughty, and would have none of them. When Finn's men came to the court the king trembled, for he was afraid that his daughter would refuse Finn as she had refused all her other suitors, and he knew Finn to be great and powerful, and he feared that he would make war against him if he did not grant his request.

But Grania had heard of the greatness of Finn, and she was pleased to think that such a great man wanted her for his wife, and she sent a message by the two men to say that she would marry him. Then Finn was very glad, and he gathered all his people and went up to the king's court to fetch Grania his wife.

But when Grania saw Finn she was dreadfully disappointed.

" He is older than my father ! " she said ; and she

was angry to think she had promised herself as a wife to an old man with grey hair.

Amongst Finn's company there was a man named Diarmid. He was the son of a great chief, and was young and strong and handsome, and when Grania saw him she fell in love with him, and secretly made up her mind to marry him instead of Finn.

So, at the feast which was held before the wedding, she drugged the wine, and everyone fell asleep except Diarmid and four of his friends. Then Grania rose up from her seat and went to Diarmid, and held out her hands to him and said :

" Oh, Diarmid, will you take my love, and carry me away from this house to-night and make me your wife ? "

Diarmid was very troubled when he heard Grania's words, for Finn was his friend, and it seemed to him that he would be betraying his friend if he did as the princess asked. And yet Grania was very beautiful, and he felt that for her love it would be almost worth while even to betray his friend.

Then in his hesitation he turned to the young men who had not drunk of the drugged wine.

" What shall I do ? " he said. " Shall I betray Finn to follow this woman and maybe bring my death upon me, or shall I keep faith with Finn and put away from me the love that Grania offers ? "

And his friends all said :

" Go with the woman, for there is nothing greater in the world than love, and you are young and strong and comely, a fitter mate for her than is Finn, for all his strength and valour."

Diarmid and Grania

Then Diarmid and Grania stole away together while Finn and his warriors and the king and his court slept.

When Finn awoke from his sleep and found Diarmid and Grania gone, he was very angry, and he called together his men and set out in pursuit of them, for he had made up his mind to kill Diarmid for his treachery and win back Grania to be his wife.

For many days and nights Grania and Diarmid fled before him. They lived in the woods, moving on from day to day, and they were always in fear lest Finn and his men should come upon them. Many times they were surrounded, and Diarmid had to fight for his life, but he was a great fighter, and always managed to escape and bring Grania safely with him too. And at last Finn got tired of pursuing Diarmid, and he made peace with him and promised to let him keep Grania for his wife, and to forgive him for stealing her away.

And after that Grania and Diarmid lived in peace together, happy and rich and contented in each other's love.

The Great Bear

ONCE, long ago, there lived a woman named Callisto. She had a little son called Arcas, and they lived together in the woods and were as happy as the day was long.

Callisto was so good and beautiful that the gods showed her great favour. Jupiter, the greatest of all the gods, was especially kind to her. But Juno, Jupiter's wife, became jealous of the lovely woman, and as she saw Callisto growing more and more beautiful every day, she determined at last to make her suffer for her loveliness and grace.

And one day, as Callisto was wandering in the forest, singing and dancing as she went because she was so happy, Juno met her, and, raising her hand, the cruel goddess turned the poor woman into an ugly rough bear.

Poor Callisto, terrified and ashamed of her ugly shape, rushed far away from her old haunts and plunged deep into the heart of the forest; and there, for fifteen long years, she lived, lonely and miserable, longing for her old companions, longing to regain her own shape, and longing, more than all, for her little son. But she dared not go back to find him, for she had lost the power of human speech when she was changed into a bear, and she was afraid that men

The Great Bear

would hunt and kill her if she ventured back to her old home.

Meanwhile, Arcas, her son, grew up tall and strong and beautiful. He was a great hunter, and one day, when he was out hunting, he went farther into the forest than he had ever been before. And there, in a little cleared space, he came across a great, rough, shaggy bear, which, though he did not know it, was really his mother, Callisto.

Callisto recognised her son at once, and stood gazing at him in longing and despair. How she wished she could speak and tell him who she really was! But she could not; and while she stood looking at him with great sorrowful eyes, Arcas fitted an arrow to his bow and took careful aim, meaning to shoot the bear.

But just as he was about to let the arrow fly, Jupiter, the great god who had been so kind to Callisto in the old happy days before she had lost her human shape, suddenly appeared in front of him, and snatching the bow and arrow from Arcas's hands, he told him who the bear really was. Jupiter had been very angry with Juno for the cruel way in which she had treated Callisto, and he had searched for the poor woman for many years in order to make amends for all she had suffered. And now he had found her, just in time to save her from being killed by her own son.

Jupiter could not change Callisto back into her human shape. Juno's power was too great for that. Besides, he was afraid that the angry goddess would hurt the poor woman further if he did so. But he was able to do something which was far better.

changed Callisto and Arcas both into stars, and
them up into the sky, where they could live
for ever and ever, and never be unhappy or sad or
lonely again.

And there on starlit nights you may see them,
shining and sparkling in the sky, the Great Bear
and the Little Bear. And there they will sparkle
and shine until the end of the world, safe from Juno's
cruelty and anger for ever.

The Seven Sleepers of Ephesus

IN the early days of Christianity there lived a Roman emperor named Decius, who persecuted the Christians from city to city and sent them to suffer cruel deaths for their faith in Christ. For this purpose he journeyed through the countries over which he ruled, and whatever city he entered he commanded that all Christians should be sought out and made to worship idols, or else be put to death.

In his journeying he came at last to Ephesus, where once more he made his cruel proclamation. Most of the Christians came forward and renounced their faith, for they had heard of the terrible sufferings Decius had inflicted in other cities. But there were seven young men at Ephesus who would not worship the idols, and they were brought before Decius and condemned to death. However, the emperor gave them one more chance for life. They should have a few days to think over their course of action, and then, if they would not renounce their faith and worship the idols, they must die.

But during these few days the seven young men managed to escape from the city. They climbed to the top of a high mountain and hid themselves in a cave, and there they determined to stay for a time until Decius left the city and the hunt for them died down.

When they were safely hidden, one of them, named Malchus, offered to go in disguise to the city and find out what was happening. He bought food and wine, and while he was making his purchases he found out that Decius was filled with fury at their escape, and, believing the young men to be hidden in the mountains, was going to send his soldiers to search for them on the morrow.

Full of fear, Malchus returned to his companions and told them the bad news. They knew that there was no escape for them, for the country round was watched by the Roman soldiers. The only thing they could do was to put their trust in God, and wait patiently for whatever might come to them.

So they ate the food that Malchus had brought, and after they had prayed they lay down to sleep, bidding each other be of good cheer, for God would protect them.

And God did indeed protect them! He sent a deep sleep upon the seven young men, and in the morning, when Decius and his soldiers searched the mountain, they still slept on.

Decius did not find them, but he saw the mouth of the cavern, and he made his soldiers block it up with stones, so that if the men he sought were within they would perish miserably with hunger.

Time passed away. Decius died and was forgotten. Christianity spread and spread until even Ephesus, the city of idolatry, was converted to the worship of Christ. It was many hundreds of years since anyone had thought of the seven young men who had tried to escape from the Roman emperor.

The Seven Sleepers of Ephesus

A man who lived at Ephesus was building a stable on the mountain which rose outside the town. And finding a pile of stones at the mouth of the cavern he took them away to use them, and so once more the light of day entered the cave. Then the seven sleepers awoke, and it seemed to them as if they had slept but a single night. They began to talk of the news Malchus had brought, and as the day wore on and nothing happened, they decided that he should go again into the town and buy some more food, and try to gather more information. So, taking a handful of coins, Malchus left the cave and began to descend the mountain.

As he drew near to the city he was astonished to see over the gate a stone cross. That had not been there when he last entered, and he rubbed his eyes, believing that he must be dreaming. But no—there it was still, and over every gate of the city he saw the same sign. Bewildered and perplexed, he passed through the gates, and as he walked along the street his amazement grew greater and greater.

" Can this indeed be Ephesus ! " he said to himself. " Yesterday no one dared to pronounce the name of Jesus ; now I hear it on everyone's lips. Can a miracle have happened in the night ? "

He stopped a passer-by and asked the name of the city, for he thought that somehow he must have made a mistake and come to the wrong town. When the man said " Ephesus," he could scarcely believe his ears. He stood still, gazing around him, and then he saw a baker's shop near by.

He entered the shop and asked for some loaves,

311

and gave the baker one of his coins. The baker examined the coin closely, and then began to whisper to some other people who were in the shop. This filled Malchus with terror. He thought that the baker recognised him, and would denounce him to the emperor.

He pulled out the rest of the money and poured it into the astonished baker's hands.

"If you will let me go you may have it all," he implored; "only do not denounce me to the wicked emperor."

The baker was very surprised at the young man's conduct. He thought that he had come dishonestly by the old coins, which were very rare and valuable by this time. He called to his companions to help him, and seizing the young man they carried him before the governor and the bishop of Ephesus, who began to examine him, trying to discover where he had found the money.

Frightened at the strangeness of the happenings, Malchus protested that he had not found them anywhere. They were his own coins, and he had brought them to buy food in the town. Then they asked him where he came from, and he answered that he was a native of Ephesus—if, indeed, this could be Ephesus.

"Who are your relatives then?" asked the governor; but when the young man gave the names of his parents no such names were known in the town. Then the governor exclaimed:

"How dare you say that this money belongs to you when it dates back so many hundreds of years? Why, it is as old as the reign of Decius, and unless you tell me at once where you found it, I will punish you with the utmost severity of the law."

"I implore you to hear me!" cried Malchus. "Answer me a few questions, I pray you—then will I endeavour to answer yours. Tell me, where is the Emperor Decius gone?"

The bishop, who had been sitting by listening, rose to his feet.

"My son, there is no emperor of that name," he said. "He who was so called died many hundreds of years ago."

Malchus stared at him in perplexity, and slowly shook his head.

"I cannot understand," he said. "All that you tell me perplexes me more and more. Follow me, and I will show you my companions who fled with me only yesterday to a cave in the mountains to escape the cruel persecutions of Decius."

The bishop turned to the governor in awe and wonder.

"The hand of God is here," he said; and he and the governor and a great crowd of the people followed Malchus to the cave. They began to remember the old story of the seven young men who had fled from the wrath of the old Roman emperor. And when they saw the young men sitting there alive and well after all those hundreds of years, they fell down on their faces and gave thanks and praise to God.

The bishop and the governor sent hurriedly for Theodosius, who was then reigning, and he hastened to Ephesus and heard the wonderful story and was taken by the inhabitants to see the martyrs in their cave. And when he saw them, he gave great glory to God.

Then one of the young men rose up and spoke to the people. He told them that doubtless God had performed this wonderful miracle in order that all that saw it should believe more firmly in the resurrection of the dead.

" God is able to restore us alive and well after all this long passage of time," he said. " Surely, then, it is in His power to restore us should we sleep for many more thousands of years."

And when he had so spoken, he and his six companions bowed their heads, and their souls returned to God.

The emperor bent over them weeping, and gave orders that golden caskets should be made to carry their bodies to Rome. But that night they appeared to him in a dream and said that as hitherto they had slept in the earth, in that same earth they desired to sleep on until God should raise them again from the dead and call them to their glorious resurrection.

The Knight of the Swan

ONCE, long ago, there lived a great duke who had one only daughter, Elsa. He loved his daughter dearly, and longed very much to see her happily married before he died, but while Elsa was still quite young he felt that his end was drawing near, and he knew that he must soon leave his dear child.

He could not bear the thought of leaving her alone and defenceless in the world, so he sent for a brave knight, a friend of his, named Frederick von Telramund, and begged him to take care of his daughter for him. Frederick promised, and the duke died with a mind set at rest about his child's future.

But Frederick was not worthy of the trust the duke had placed in him. When he saw how beautiful Elsa was he wanted her for his wife, and one day he asked the girl to marry him, saying that her father had promised him her hand before he died.

Elsa knew that this was not true. She did not love the knight, brave and rich and great though he was, and she refused to marry him.

" My father would not have me marry a man who breaks his faith," she said proudly, and she tried to avoid the false knight as much as she could.

When Frederick saw that Elsa would not have

315

anything to do with him he appealed to the emperor, and the emperor, thinking that the knight had right on his side, gave him permission to fight for Elsa in the lists against any champion that Elsa should choose. He appointed a day for the ordeal to take place, and then, if Elsa's champion overthrew Frederick von Telramund, she should be free ; but if, on the other hand, Frederick should be the conqueror, then he should have the right to take Elsa and marry her, whether she would or no.

In the old days people thought a great deal of these trials of strength. They thought that God would send help to the man whose cause was just, and they were ready and willing to abide by the decision, whatever it might be.

It seemed this time as though Frederick von Telramund had right on his side, for not a single knight would come forward to fight for Elsa. As the day approached the poor girl became almost ill with grief and despair, and when at last the lists were opened and she was obliged to go to the place where the tournament was to be held, she knew that the result was a foregone conclusion. She had no champion to fight for her; the emperor and all the people would say that she lied when she declared that her father had never promised her hand to Frederick, and she would be obliged to marry this man whom she feared and hated so much.

The place where the trial was to be held was by the banks of the river. There were thick woods all around, but there was one broad clear space where the tournaments took place. On one side was the emperor, surrounded by his knights and heralds, and on the other, alone and solitary, with not a single friend beside her, stood Elsa, pale and sad, but still steadfast in her determination to hold out until she was forced to yield to the fate in store for her.

The heralds blew their trumpets and Frederick von Telramund rode out into the lists, spear in hand, ready to do battle against anyone who might come. Then the heralds blew again for Elsa's champion to come out and vindicate her claim, but no one appeared. Again they blew, and Frederick laughed scornfully as again no one came forward.

"Is there none to fight for you, fair lady?" he cried. "If your cause were just surely Heaven itself would raise up a champion to prove it."

A third and last time the heralds blew, and suddenly on the river a strange sight appeared. A beautiful white swan came floating down with the tide, drawing behind it a little silver boat, and in the boat lay a knight in armour, asleep upon his shield. The swan drew the boat to land, and the moment it reached the shore the knight awoke and sprang upon the bank. Then the swan sailed away again with its boat, and the knight turned to the emperor and the astonished people and said that he had come to fight for Elsa against the man who had so falsely betrayed his trust.

Elsa joyfully accepted him for her champion, and the stranger, having been provided with a horse, the duel began.

Fiercely Frederick bore down upon the unknown knight, but Elsa's champion proved himself a warrior of skill and courage, and after a long and terrible struggle the knight of the swan prevailed. Frederick was overthrown, and Elsa was delivered from the marriage which was so hateful to her.

The strange knight rode up to Elsa when the fight was over, and knelt before her, and Elsa, her heart overflowing with joy and thankfulness and love, held out her hands towards him.

"You have won me worthily, sir knight," she said. "Now, if you will, I give you my hand in marriage and all that I possess."

"Willingly will I accept the gift, gracious lady," replied the knight; "but there is one condition that I must make. Never must you ask me whence I come or what my lineage is. My name is Lohengrin, this only can I tell you."

Elsa was so much in love with her brave young champion that she felt she did not care who he was as long as he was hers. She willingly agreed to the knight's conditions, and the very same day the two were married.

For a long time they lived together very happily. Lohengrin proved a brave and devoted husband, and Elsa grew to love him more and more. There was only one thing that prevented her from being perfectly happy, and that was that she might never know anything of the life her husband led before she married him. She did not mind for her own sake, but when she heard other people whispering amongst themselves as to Lohengrin's supposed origin, it grieved her that she could not speak out in his defence.

One day she overheard a malicious rumour about

her husband, which worried her very much. And that night Lohengrin awoke from his sleep to find his wife sobbing beside him.

"My love, what is it? What ails thee?" he cried; but Elsa would not tell him.

The next night the same thing happened, yet still Elsa would give no reason for her tears; but on the third night, when again Lohengrin awoke and found her crying, she could keep back the question that was troubling her no longer.

"Husband, be not angry with me," she sobbed, "but I can bear it no longer. Tell me who you are and whence you came?"

Lohengrin rose very sadly, and looked down at the wife he loved so dearly.

"I come from far away, from the temple of the Holy Grail, where with other chosen knights I tended the sacred vessel. When the hour of your trial drew near the temple bell began to toll, untouched by human hands, a sure sign that an innocent soul was in some sore distress. I was chosen to go forth and fight for truth and justice, and as I waited, not knowing whither to ride, the swan appeared on the river, drawing the boat which brought me to you. Only so long as you did not ask me whence I came was I permitted to stay with you. Now I must go back to the holy place."

Then he kissed his wife tenderly and gave her his sword and ring, and told her never to part with them. Elsa clung to him, weeping bitterly, begging him not to leave her, but it was no use. Lohengrin told her that he must go as soon as he was sent for.

" Which will not be long now," he said.

Just as the day began to dawn, the swan that had brought the stranger knight to Elsa's rescue appeared on the river which ran by the castle walls, drawing the silver boat. With one last good-bye to his weeping wife, Lohengrin stepped into the little vessel. The swan sailed away down the river, and that was the last that was ever seen of the knight of the swan.

The Country of the Young

OISIN was the son of Finn, the great Irish hero. He was a great fighter, too, and a maker of poems and a leader of men, and he fought many battles beside his father and his father's mighty men.

One misty morning Finn and Oisin and the men of the Fianna were out hunting on the borders of a lake, and as they hunted they saw coming towards them a beautiful young woman riding upon a white horse.

She had a crown on her head and wore a long silk cloak embroidered with golden stars, and her eyes were blue and misty like the sea, and her hair was long and soft and golden, and fell down over the folds of her cloak.

She came to where Finn was standing and then drew rein, and Finn looked at her, and marvelling at her beauty, asked her who she was and whither she came.

"I have come from the Country of the Young, O King of the Fianna," she said; "and my name is Niamh, and I am a king's daughter. And it is to Oisin your son that I have come. For I have heard of his great name and his great deeds, and I have set my love upon him."

v   321

Then Oisin came up and put his hand upon her horse's bridle, and as he gazed into her lovely eyes he fell in love with her, so that he felt that the sunshine and gladness would go out of all the world unless he could have her for his wife.

" What would you have of me ? " he said; and Niamh, bending down, answered :

" I would have you be my husband and come away with me to the Country of the Young."

" I will go with you," said Oisin; and he kissed his father and said good-bye to the rest of the Fianna, and sprang upon the horse behind the beautiful woman. And the horse shook himself and neighed three times, and rode off westward into the sea.

Over the waves of the sea the horse galloped as easily as though it had been on dry land. It bore its riders onward for many days, and they passed through strange countries and saw many wonderful things, until at last they came to the country from which Niamh had come. And a wonderful country it was.

The trees were covered with fruit and leaves and blossom all at the same time, flowers were blooming everywhere, and the grass was greener and fresher even than it is in Ireland. It was always summer in that country, and the people who lived there were always young and strong and happy. No sickness or sorrow or death ever came there, but all was laughing and rejoicing and feasting and singing the whole day long.

The king of the country came out himself to welcome Oisin, and young maidens came with singing

The Country of the Young

and dancing to bring him into the king's palace, which was built of gold and shining stones. And Oisin was married to Niamh, the king's daughter, and for many years he lived with her in perfect happiness. Yet for all the years were so many, they seemed to him to be but the passing of a few days.

But at last a great longing filled his heart to go back to his father and the men with whom he had lived and fought and hunted all his life, and at length he asked Niamh to let him go back to Ireland and see his friends again. But Niamh was sad when she heard his desire.

" You may go," she said; " but oh, Oisin, I am afraid that you will never come back to me and my country again."

" If you will lend me your white horse," said Oisin, " he will surely bring me back again to you. For it is not in Ireland I want to be staying, only just to see Finn, my father, and my friends once more."

Niamh shook her head sorrowfully.

" I have great fear," she said. " Yet will I let you go, and you shall have the white horse to bear you. But mind that while you are away you never put one foot to the ground. If you dismount from the horse's back, even for one moment, you will never come back to the Country of the Young."

Then she kissed him and let him go, and Oisin mounted the horse and set his face towards Ireland.

After many days and nights the horse brought Oisin to his native land, but when he looked around him he could find no trace of Finn and the Fianna.

The people were strangers to him, and even the country-side seemed changed.

As he sat there on his horse, staring around him in bewilderment, he saw a group of peasants working in a field close by, and he rode up to them and asked them if they could tell him where Finn and the Fianna had gone. The peasants stared at him when he asked them that question, and they said :

" We have often heard of Finn that lived so long ago. He was the greatest man in all Ireland, and there are many books and poems made about him by the poets of Ireland, and it would be hard for us to tell you all of them. But as for Finn and his men, they are gone long ago now, and no man knows where it is they lie sleeping."

Then Oisin turned away, very sad and sorrowful at heart, for he saw that the time which had passed so pleasantly for him in the Country of the Young had been as long as many hundreds of years in the world he had left.

And, full of grief, he rode his horse to the place where Finn's great hall had stood, and when he saw no sign at all of it, and nothing but weeds and nettles growing there, the tears came into his eyes and ran down his face.

He was just turning away to start back on his journey, when suddenly, amongst the weeds and nettles, he saw a stone trough lying. It was the one in which Finn and his men had been used to wash their hands when they returned from the hunt, and when he saw it a great longing came into Oisin's heart to dip his

The Country of the Young

hands in the water that was lying in it, as he had used to do in the happy days of old.

Forgetting what Niamh had told him, he sprang from his horse, and in a moment all the years he had lived came upon him, and he fell upon the ground, a weak, feeble old man, without sight, without shape, and without any comeliness of mind or face or body.

As for the horse, that had disappeared altogether, and Oisin never saw him or the beautiful country he had come from any more.

And that is the story of Oisin's visit to the Country of the Young.

Orion and His Dog

IN those old days, when the gods so often came to earth, there lived a mighty hunter named Orion. He had a faithful dog called Sirius, who followed him wherever he went, and all day long the two roamed the forest together in search of game for the hunter's bow.

One day Orion came across a group of young girls in the forest. They were the Seven Pleiades, and were some of Diana's handmaidens; and, frightened at the approach of a human being, they rushed away with cries of terror.

But the hunter Orion, half in fun and half in earnest, ran after them. He was fleet of foot, and he would easily have caught them, but the maidens called to their mistress to save them. Diana heard their prayer, and just as Orion caught them up they were suddenly changed into seven snow-white pigeons, and flew out of his reach towards the sky. Up and up and up they flew, until at last they touched the blue of the sky itself, and then Diana turned them into stars that they might shine for ever in the firmament.

It was fortunate for Orion that Diana did not punish him for thus frightening her maidens. (Perhaps she would have been more severe if Orion had not been a hunter. Diana was passionately fond of hunting herself, and so had a fellow-feeling for the young man. After she discovered how skilful he was in the chase, Diana often went with him on his hunting expeditions, and they soon became great friends together.

But Apollo, Diana's twin brother, did not like to see his sister, the great goddess of the moon, the companion of a mortal, and he made a plan to separate the two friends. One day he called Diana to him, and began to talk to her of her favourite sport—shooting with the bow and arrow.

"They tell me that your skill at archery exceeds the skill of all the other gods, sister," he said. "Let me see how accurately you can shoot?" And pointing to a dark speck rising and falling far out on the sea, the sun-god told Diana to take that as her target.

Now the dark speck was really the head of Orion, who was refreshing himself with a swim in the cool sea water. Apollo knew this, for he had seen the swimmer as he drove in his chariot across the sky; but Diana did not know, and she never suspected that her brother was deceiving her. Seizing her bow, she fitted an arrow to the string, and, taking careful aim, discharged it full at the dark speck. The dark speck vanished beneath the waves, for so true had been Diana's aim that the arrow had struck Orion full on the forehead and killed him at once.

When Diana found out that she had killed her chosen friend and playmate she was full of grief and distress. For many days she mourned for lost Orion, shedding bitter tears over him and longing to be able to bring him back to life. But goddess though she was, she was not able to make him alive again.

But though she could not bring him back to life, there was one thing she could do for her friend, which was better even than that. Diana changed Orion and his faithful dog Sirius into stars, and carried them up to the sky that they might shine at night, and so live on in men's hearts and minds for ever.

The Golden Touch

IF somebody came to you and said that you could ask whatever you liked and your wish would be granted, what do you think you would wish for ? I hope you would not be like King Midas, who, when for some service he had rendered to Bacchus, the god of wine, was told that he might choose anything in the world he liked as a reward, asked that everything he touched should be turned to gold.

King Midas was really a very foolish king indeed. He thought that gold was the best thing in the world, and although he owned a good deal of it already, yet he was far from being satisfied, and he was always thinking and planning how he could get some more. So when Bacchus said with a smile that his wish should be granted he was overjoyed, and he hurried home to his palace to begin the pleasant task of turning everything he possessed into gold.

As he passed through his garden he saw the roses which grew there, red and white and pink and yellow, and he thought to himself that here would be a good opportunity to try if it was really true—if the gift of the golden touch was really his.

To his delight, no sooner had he touched the flowers than they were turned to purest gold, as were also the

329

leaves and stems, and even the blades of grass upon which he walked.

Full of joy Midas hurried into his palace and began the work of changing all his belongings into gold—the chairs and the tables, the statues in his great hall, the vases of flowers, the ornaments; every single thing that he could lay his hands on he changed into shining gold.

King Midas felt that he had indeed obtained his heart's desire. He would be the richest king that ever had been; for if in a few hours he had succeeded in turning so many comparatively worthless things into the precious metal, what would not his wealth be at the end of a few years! His palace would be the wonder and the marvel of the whole world by the time he had finished with it.

After a time he became hungry, for he had been working hard exercising the magic touch, and he was glad to see that his servants were bringing in a meal. He sat down in his golden chair to his golden table, and laying his hands on the plates and dishes changed them in a moment to vessels of almost priceless worth.

But, alas! King Midas had forgotten that it was not only plates and dishes and tables and chairs that would turn to gold in his hand. Everything that he touched must be transformed in this way too, and to his horror he found that he was unable to take the smallest bite of anything. Whatever he tried to eat, no sooner did it touch his lips than it turned to a lump of solid gold! And it was just the same when he tried to drink. One moment his goblet seemed full of delicious sparkling wine, but the moment he lifted it to his lips the liquid was changed to a mass of gold.

King Midas sat aghast. What use was the wonderful gift to him if everything he tried to eat was turned to gold ? If he could not eat he must surely die, and then what would be the good of all his treasures ? It seemed that he hàd not made such a wise choice after all.

While he was sitting in the midst of all his splendour his little daughter came into the room. In her hand she held one of the golden roses which King Midas had transformed with such pleasure only a short time before, but instead of seeming pleased with it she was sobbing bitterly.

King Midas loved his little daughter dearly, and the sight of her grief made him forget his own troubles for the moment.

" What is the matter, little one ? " he said kindly, and the child held up the golden rose.

" Somebody has been hurting my lovely roses," she sobbed. " Every single one of them has been turned into this horrible cold, ugly stuff."

King Midas could not find a word to comfort her. He was beginning to think of the gold as horrible cold, ugly stuff too ! He could only hold out his arms to his little daughter, and take her on his knees and try to console her for her grief.

But once again he had forgotten the golden touch. He lifted on to his knee a warm living human child— he found in his arms nothing but a little gold statue !

You can imagine the poor father's distress. He kissed the little girl, and cried over her, and called to

her, but it was all no use, and at last springing up
he hurried out of his palace to find the god Bacchus
to beg him to take away the terrible gift he had
granted him.

Perhaps Bacchus felt sorry for the poor, foolish king,
or perhaps he thought it would not do for a mortal to
possess for long such a magic power. At any rate, he
had pity upon poor Midas, and he told him that if he
washed in a certain river the power of the golden
touch would go from him, and that he might restore
to its original shape anything he had changed by
sprinkling it with the water.

So the story of the golden touch ended happily after
all. The king made haste to bathe himself in the
river : then hurrying home he changed his little daughter
back again into her own little warm living self, and after
that he did not think nearly so much of his riches as
he had done before.

But the sands of the river in which King Midas
bathed to rid himself of the golden touch sparkled like
shining gold for ever after.

Lady Godiva

THERE once lived in the town of Coventry a great and powerful earl who was very cruel and hard to the people over whom he ruled. He loved money, and in order to get it he laid huge taxes upon the town—taxes which grew yearly heavier and heavier until it became impossible for the people to go on paying them. And at last there arose such great distress in Coventry that the people came to their hard ruler and begged him to take off the tax that was ruining them all. Mothers brought their little ones to the castle gates and held them up to show how starved and ill they were, and cried for mercy, saying that if they paid any more money they must surely die of hunger.

The cruel earl did not heed the cries of the people. He sat in his great hall and laughed, and refused to take a penny off the tax.

"Let them starve!" he said when he heard what the poor mothers were crying out.

But there was one person in the castle who heard the cries of the starving people, and, hearing them, heeded. Godiva, the earl's young wife, was fair and beautiful, and as tender-hearted as he was cruel and hard. She could not bear to think of the way in which her people were suffering, and at last she went to her husband and begged him to repeal the tax.

"If they pay it, they will starve," she said with tears in her eyes. "And all the poor little babies—oh! husband, they are so weak and sick and ailing."

The earl stared at his wife in amazement. He loved her in his own rough way, for she was always dutiful and obedient, but she had always seemed so timid and frightened of him that he had never dreamt that she would dare to question anything he did. He did not know at first whether to be angry with her or not, and he said roughly:

"What do these people matter to you? You needn't worry your pretty little head about *them.* Why —you wouldn't let your little finger ache for such as these!"

"Oh, but I would!" she cried, clasping her hands in distress. "I would do anything—*anything*—to help them! Only try me, and see if I will not be willing to perform any task, however difficult it may be, if you will only repeal the tax!"

The earl looked at her for a moment, then he laughed—a cruel, mocking laugh.

"Well, I will set you a task," he said. "Ride you through the town naked—and I repeal the tax!"

Then, with a scornful smile at his wife's horror-stricken face, he strode from the great hall, his mocking laughter echoing amongst the lofty rafters.

Left alone, Godiva stood aghast. She couldn't—*couldn't* do that—not even to save her starving people. Ride naked through the town—surely her lord did not, could not, really mean her to do that? But he did mean it—in her heart of hearts she knew well that he meant it; but he never for one moment thought

Lady Godiva

that she would do it. It was because he knew how she would shrink in horror and disgust from such an action that he had thought himself safe in setting her that task.

As she stood there fighting with herself, trying to stifle her feelings of pity, trying to persuade herself that no one could possibly expect her to do a thing like that, the thought of the little weak, sickly babies, lying so feebly in their mothers' arms, came to her again. And suddenly her heart began to burn with a great courage.

" I *will* do it ! " she said aloud. " For their sakes I will do it ! "

Quickly, lest she should change her mind again, she called a herald to her side and sent him out into the town to proclaim the condition upon which the earl had declared he would take away the tax. And she told the herald to bid all the people go into their houses and fasten their shutters, and not come out again until the clock struck twelve, as she had determined to make the sacrifice and win freedom for them. Then she gave orders that in an hour's time her horse was to be brought, bridled and saddled, and left at the gateway ready for her to mount; and when that was done she ordered that all her servants should go far away to the other side of the castle, and not venture to set foot through the halls and passages again until the clock struck twelve. Then, having done all that she could to hide her coming shame from every eye, she went to her own room and began to undress.

Soon she was ready, and, naked from head to foot,

except for her long hair which hung down nearly to her knees, she crept from her chamber and stole silently down the castle stairs. She reached the gateway and found her horse ready and waiting as she had commanded, and hastily mounting, she began her ride through the streets of the city.

It was a terrible ordeal for her. The houses seemed full of staring eyes, the sound of a dog's bark brought the hot colour into her cheeks ; even her horse's footfall made her heart beat quicker. But everything comes to an end, and at last that dreadful ride was over. The castle gateway came in sight, and just as the great clocks in the town crashed out the hour of noon, she slipped from her horse's back and fled through the long corridors, gaining her own room in safety, unseen by any human eye.

The legend says that one man, filled with curiosity, dead to all feelings of honour and gratitude, made himself a peep-hole from which he might see the earl's wife as she rode by. But just as her horse's hoofs were heard in the street, and before he could catch a glimpse of Lady Godiva herself, he was suddenly stricken with blindness as a punishment for daring to do such a wicked, ungrateful thing.

So Lady Godiva won freedom for the town of Coventry. For the earl kept his word and repealed the hard tax in honour of his brave wife, who had dared so much to save and help her people, and had won for herself a name which was loved and honoured through all generations.

Tannhäuser

A KNIGHT was once riding through the fields and valleys of Germany, on his way to a city where a great contest of singers was to be held. This knight's name was Tannhäuser. He was a famous minstrel, and he was riding to take part in the contest, hoping to gain the prize.

As the dusk was falling his way led him by the foot of a high mountain. The mountain cut off the last rays of the setting sun and threw a deep shadow over the road, but as the singer pressed forward the gloom was suddenly brightened by a gleam of rosy light. A strain of sweet music filled the air, and before Tannhäuser's astonished eyes appeared a woman of such exquisite beauty that his heart almost stopped still with wonder.

It was Venus, the goddess of love and beauty. She smiled at the knight, and beckoning him to follow her, she turned and led the way up the mountain-side.

For one moment Tannhäuser hesitated. He was a Christian knight, and he knew that he ought not to follow the pagan goddess. But the strains of the wonderful music drew him on, and springing from his horse he hastened after the lovely figure. And as he went the handmaidens of the goddess scattered roses

W 337

before him, so that he seemed to be treading on a pathway of magic flowers.

The goddess beckoned him on until she reached the entrance of a cave in the mountain-side. With one more smile at the knight she disappeared through the dark doorway, and Tannhäuser, throwing all caution to the winds, plunged after her. No sooner had he entered than the door closed behind him, and he descended down into the heart of the mountain to the palace where Venus lived.

For seven years he lived in the mountain, seven years in which he forgot all his Christian vows, all his knightly deeds, all that was good and pure and true. He spent the time in feasting and revelling, in worship of the goddess who had allured him into her palace, finding all his joy in song and wine and music and heathen luxury.

But at the end of the seven years Tannhäuser's heart began to stir within him. He sickened of the perpetual singing and dancing and feasting, and he began to long for the fresh, pure breezes of earth, for the blue sky, for the still stars at night, for his old life of noble chivalry. He thought with horror and loathing of the worship he had given to Venus, and he longed to be absolved from his sin that he might worship God again in pureness of mind and heart.

He went to Venus and begged her to let him go, but Venus was deaf to his imploring prayers. He had followed her into the mountain of his own free will, she said. Now he was hers, and she would not let him go. And Tannhäuser could not escape without her permission, for none could pass through the cavern doors unless she willed.

Bitterly repentant now, the knight passed his days in grief and misery. He thought of his past life, and he longed to be free that he might make atonement for his sin. And then at last, in his despair, he fell upon his knees and cried to the Virgin Mother for help.

It was the first time since he had entered the mountain of Venus that any real prayer had passed his lips, and in a moment it was answered. A sudden rift appeared in the mountain-side, and, rushing forth, Tannhäuser found himself again above the ground, with the fresh sweet morning air blowing upon his face once more.

Overcome with joy he flung himself down upon the soft cool grass, still wet with dew, and tears of happiness fell from his eyes. He gathered handfuls of the little heather flowers that grew on the mountain, and he looked with love and thankfulness at the blue sky which had been hidden from him for so many weary years.

It was on a Sunday morning when he was released from his prison-house, and as he lay there on the mountain-top the bells of a little church below in the valley began to ring for service. Tannhäuser sprang to his feet and hurried down to the village. He entered the church doors and sought out the priest, and there, kneeling in God's temple, he made his terrible confession, and prayed the priest to grant him absolution for his sin.

But the priest was horror-stricken at his story.

He did not dare to give the stranger absolution, for he doubted whether there could be forgiveness for one who had forsaken the true God to worship at the shrine of a pagan goddess. He sent the penitent knight to another priest, and there once more Tannhäuser told his story and begged for absolution, but once more the priest dared not give it. He sent him on to another, and for a long time Tannhäuser was passed on from village to village, from town to town, until at last he was sent to Rome to see the Pope himself.

The Pope at that time was a hard, cold man, and he exclaimed in horror when he heard of Tannhäuser's guilt.

"How dare you ask for forgiveness!" he cried. "Guilt such as thine can never be remitted. Sooner shall this staff in my hand grow green and blossom than that God should pardon thee!"

Tannhäuser rose and went away, his heart sick and miserable. He had thought to find forgiveness, but it seemed there was no forgiveness for a sinner as stained with sin as he was. Full of despair, he turned back again towards the mountain of Venus. If there was no place for him in earth or heaven, at least there was an abode for him here.

But a miracle happened. Three days after he had gone the Pope's attendants came rushing into his room to arouse him. In the night his staff, the symbol of his office, had put forth buds and had burst into flowers!

Covered with remorse, the Pope sent messengers in hot haste after Tannhäuser. But it was too late;

Tannhäuser

the messengers reached the little village at the foot of the mountain only to hear that a man with bowed head and a face worn and haggard with misery had entered the cavern that led to the palace of Venus a few hours before.

That is the story of Tannhäuser so far as we know it, but I do not think that that is the whole of it really. I am sure that a man on whose behalf such a wonderful miracle had been performed would never have been allowed to return for ever to the life of sin and wickedness which had grown to be such a burden to him.

And I think that when the time comes for the end of all the unfinished stories in the world to be known, we shall find that this one too—with all other sad stories—has had after all a happy ending.

St. Andrew of Scotland

ST. ANDREW, the brave champion of Scotland, like all the other brave Christian knights who lived in the world long ago, journeyed from land to land in search of adventures, doing noble deeds and carrying tidings of the Cross of Christ wherever he went.

It happened one night as he journeyed that he came into a dark and gloomy valley where he had never been before, and where there were so many winding paths that he lost his way. All around him he could hear the roaring of wild beasts, and for a little while he was almost in despair. He was afraid that he would not be able to find his way out of this dreadful place in the thick darkness, and he knew that only a miracle could save him if he were obliged to pass the night in the midst of so many terrible dangers.

But in his peril he remembered the God in whose cause he had always fought so bravely, and, kneeling down, he prayed that he might be delivered from this place of terror. Or, if that should not be Heaven's will, that he might be given courage and strength to meet his death as a Christian knight should.

As he prayed he saw before him a gleaming light that moved backwards and forwards in the darkness as though beckoning him to follow. And St. Andrew,

St. Andrew of Scotland

believing that Heaven had indeed sent him the aid for which he had prayed, rose from his knees and, mounting his horse, followed the guiding light. And when the dawn began to break he found himself out of the dreadful valley, in a pleasant fertile country where birds sang and flowers grew and the wind blew soft and sweet.

St. Andrew rode on until he came to a great castle, into which he entered, hoping to find food and shelter and welcome. But inside the castle gates he found mourning and weeping, and when he asked the cause of all this sorrow he heard a sad story.

The king who lived in the castle had six lovely daughters, whom he loved passionately. A wicked giant had captured the maidens and would have carried them away to his castle to keep them in slavery for the rest of their lives. But as he bore them away they were suddenly changed into six white swans, with crowns of gold on their heads, and had fluttered out of his hands. They had escaped the horrible fate the giant had destined for them, and had returned to their father's kingdom, but it seemed that nothing could restore them to their former shape. Seven years had passed away, and though the king and his subjects had prayed constantly to all the gods they knew, the maidens had not yet been delivered from their strange enchantment. They were safe in their father's kingdom, but it seemed as though they were doomed for ever to swim mournfully up and down the river that ran by the castle walls, in the form of six white swans.

On Sundays their father offered up prayers and sacrifices to the sun, on Mondays to the moon. On

Tuesdays he prayed to the god Mars, on Wednesdays to Mercury, on Thursdays to Eros, on Fridays to Venus, and on Saturdays to Saturn. But none of these gods had power to hear or grant the king's prayer, and all his fasting and mourning and weeping and sacrifice was in vain.

When St. Andrew had heard the story of the six white swans he was filled with pity for their unhappy fate, and standing up boldly before the court he told the king and the people that it was useless for them to pray to their false gods any longer. He told them that there was only one true God, and that doubtless it was He who had heard the cry of the maidens as the giant carried them away, and had changed them into swans. And he said that no doubt He was waiting now for the king to offer up his petitions to the throne of Heaven before He would allow them to regain their former shape.

As St. Andrew finished speaking these words, there was an angry murmur from the people round. And all the knights of the king's court sprang forward, begging the king to let them do battle with the strange knight who spoke against the honour of their gods.

Though he was only one knight against many, St. Andrew accepted their challenge, trusting to the righteousness of his cause and the strength of his God to enable him to prevail.

The fight was fixed for the next day, and all that night St. Andrew spent in prayer and in preparation for the coming conflict. Then in the morning he buckled on his armour, mounted his horse, and rode out to the appointed place, ready to do battle against all that might come.

St. Andrew of Scotland

He looked a brave and worthy knight as he waited, his armour shining in the sunlight, bearing in blue silk the silver cross of Scotland on his breast. He trusted not in his own strength, but in the strength of the God who had so often given him the victory. One by one the pagan knights entered the lists against him, but one by one they retired vanquished, for none could stand against the might of the Christian champion's victorious lance.

The heathen knights were enraged at St. Andrew's strength and skill, and, forgetting all the laws of chivalry, they rode at him together, seeking to bear him down by sheer force of numbers. But it seemed as though the Christian knight bore a charmed life, for though he received many a grievous hurt and wound, yet none could vanquish him, and at last the king called his knights away and hailed St. Andrew as the conqueror.

"Thy God is indeed more mighty than all the gods I have worshipped," he said; "from henceforth He shall be my God too." And kissing St. Andrew's sword he vowed to become a Christian.

And as he vowed the six swans suddenly raised their wings and flew on to the banks of the river. And no sooner had they touched the ground than they regained their human form and ran to embrace their father, hailing St. Andrew as their champion and deliverer.

You can imagine what joy there was in that country, and how the people praised and blessed St. Andrew for his skill and bravery. But what pleased the brave knight most of all was that the people forsook their old false gods and turned to the worship of the one true

345

God, who had saved St. Andrew though all the knights and warriors of the king's court had been arrayed against him.

St. Andrew rested at the castle until he had recovered from his wounds, and then rode out into the world again in search of another noble quest, rejoicing that he had been able to fight so valiantly for his faith, and had been the means of turning so many people to Christianity.

The Pied Piper of Hamelin

ONCE upon a time, many hundreds of years ago, the town of Hamelin, in Brunswick, was overrun with a plague of rats. They swarmed everywhere, in the kitchens and in the bedrooms, in the attics and in the basements. They fought with the dogs, they killed the cats, they bit the children, they broke open the casks of provisions, they ate up everything in the houses, and even grew so bold as to lick the soup from the very ladles the cooks were using.

The people tried everything they could think of to get rid of them, but nothing was of any use. The number of rats grew greater every day, and at last matters began to grow serious.

One day, when the townspeople were growing desperate, a strange man came through the streets of Hamelin. He was dressed in the quaintest clothes, half yellow and half red, and round his neck hung a pipe.

The people stopped and stared at the strange-looking man and wondered who he could be. When they asked him who he was, the man said that he was called the Pied Piper, because of his queer dress and the magic power that lay in his pipe.

"I can draw all creatures living beneath the sun after me if I will," he said. "And if you will give me a thousand guilders I will rid your town of rats."

The people agreed at once to the Piper's terms, and then waited eagerly to see what he would do.

The Piper raised his pipe to his lips and began to play. And as he played there was heard a faint muttering, which grew and grew until, with a noise like thunder, the rats came pouring out of the houses, young rats, old rats, grey rats, black rats, rats of every possible size and colour. They pressed after the Piper, drawn by the strange spell of the music, and the Piper led them from street to street, until they came to the river, into which they plunged and were every one of them drowned.

Overjoyed, the people of Hamelin hurried back to their houses and began to poke out the nests and block up the holes, and try to get rid of the traces of the rats. They set all the church bells ringing and went about with joyful faces, congratulating one another on having at last got rid of the horrible plague.

In the midst of all this rejoicing the Piper was forgotten. In spite of the people being so pleased to be free of the rats, they did not worry at all about the man who had freed the town from them, and when at last the Piper ventured to ask for the money they had promised, they refused to give it to him.

They thought because the rats were drowned that it did not matter whether they kept their promise or not.

"What is dead can't come to life again," they said, and they laughed at the Piper, and told him to go away and not bother any more.

Then the Piper grew very angry, and warned them that they would be sorry if they did not give him the

The Pied Piper of Hamelin

money they had promised. But still the people laughed
and treated his words as idle threats, and at last the
Piper turned away.

But he did not leave Hamelin. Instead, he stepped
once more into the streets and raised his pipe to his lips
and began to play the softest, sweetest, gayest tune
that ever was heard.

And as the notes of the music rose on the air there
came a sound of rustling and bustling, the pattering of
little feet, the clapping of little hands and the chattering
of little voices, and from every house and cottage in
the town out came the children running.

They hurried after the Piper, laughing and dancing
and shouting for joy, while the people of Hamelin
stood still in horror, unable to move a step or speak a
word to save their children.

They had never dreamt that the Piper would be
able to do anything so dreadful as this or they would
have kept their promise and given him the money.
They watched in an agony of terror as he led their
little ones through the streets. Was he going to drown
them all as he had drowned the rats?

But no, as he reached the river's brink the Piper
turned, and, still playing his wonderful music, he led the
children out of the town to the foot of a mountain
which stood close by. As they came near a door in
the mountain-side swung open, revealing a wonderful
cavern, into which the Piper advanced. The children
followed, and when all were inside the door swung to
again and shut fast.

Of all the merry throng of children who followed
the Piper that day only one came back to Hamelin,

and that was a poor little lame boy who could not keep
up with the others, and so found himself shut outside
the magic door. He cried bitterly at being left behind,
but when people asked him what there was in the Piper's
music to make the children follow him, he could not
tell them. He only knew that the music spoke to him
of a wonderful country in which everything was new
and strange and beautiful, where there was no sorrow
or sadness, and where his poor lame foot would be quite
cured.

Alas for the people of Hamelin! If the Piper had
appeared again they would have given him all the gold
they possessed if he would only have brought back their
children. But though they sent messengers through
every land and offered great rewards to anyone who
should bring tidings of him, they never again heard of
the Pied Piper.

And nobody ever knew what became of the children.
Some people said that the Piper led them through a
subterranean passage and brought them out into another
part of the world, where they lived to grow up into
men and women, and became a nation by themselves.
But nobody ever found out for certain. And I myself
always like to think that the Piper really did take the
children to the wonderful country he promised them,
and that perhaps they are playing happily there to this
very day.

The Legend of the Mistletoe

BALDER was the fairest of all the sons of Odin. He was as good as he was beautiful, and because he was so good and happy and bright he was beloved by everyone, not only by the gods and goddesses that lived in Asgard, but by all men and women who lived in the world as well.

One night Balder dreamt a terrible dream that filled him with trouble and distress, and in the morning he told Frigga, his mother, about it. And when Frigga heard it she, too, became anxious and troubled, for she feared that it was a warning of some danger that was threatening her best beloved son.

So she went out in the world and made everything she found there promise not to hurt Balder. From fire and wood and earth and water, from stones and metal, from birds and beasts and all creeping things, she asked the promise, and because everything in the world loved Balder for his brightness and goodness they all gave their word not to hurt or injure him in any way.

Then Frigga went back to Asgard satisfied, for she knew that none of the things that had promised would break their vow.

When the other gods found that nothing could now hurt Balder they began to throw things at him in play, laughing to see how they all turned aside from the bright young god. Nothing could hurt him, whatever they threw at him—swords, battle-axes, spears, darts, great stones that would have crushed any other man to death in an instant, all passed by Balder as harmlessly as though they were flakes of snow or petals of flowers. It soon became one of the recognised games in Asgard to get Balder to stand up and act as a target, while the other gods tried their skill at hurling their weapons at him. And Balder laughed and enjoyed it as much as the others did.

But Loki, the god of fire, was jealous of Balder, and he could not bear to see him so happy and popular with everyone. And an evil thought came into his heart that if he could only find one thing that had not taken the vow not to hurt Balder, he might be able to have revenge on him for being so good and beautiful and well beloved.

Now there was one thing that Frigga had forgotten, and that was a little harmless plant called the mistletoe, which grew on the eastern side of the palace of Valhalla. She had remembered it afterwards, but she thought that it was so weak and feeble that it could not hurt Balder even if it wished to, and so she had not troubled to go again and ask it to make the promise too. And wicked Loki came to know of this, and his evil heart rejoiced, for now he began to see a way to carry out his plans.

He went to the eastern gate of Valhalla and cut down the mistletoe plant, and then from its strongest stem he made an arrow, so sharp and strong that he was sure it could not fail to do what he wished.

352

The Legend of the Mistletoe

Then he went back to where the gods were playing with Balder, hurling their knives and spears at him, and laughing to see how they glanced harmlessly from his beautiful body.

Balder had a brother, Höder, who was quite blind, and was often very sad and gloomy, but who loved his bright, beautiful young brother with a love that was perhaps all the stronger for his own sadness and sorrow. He could not take part in the games with Balder which all the other gods loved to play, but he always stood as close as he might, listening to the merry laughter, and wishing, oh! so intensely, that he might be able to see, if only for one moment, the young brother who was so dear and sweet and precious to him.

As he stood there on the evening when Loki was making his wicked plans, the god of fire saw him, and crept up to his side.

" Why do you not join in the sport to do honour to Balder ? " asked Loki, though he knew very well why poor Höder did not.

" Because I am blind," said Höder. " I cannot see where Balder stands, and beside, I have nothing to throw at him."

" As for that," said the wicked god, " that need not trouble you. Here is an arrow—take that and throw it at him, and I will direct your aim towards the place where he stands. It is only right that you should take part in the sport to do honour to Balder, too."

Then Höder, never guessing what was in Loki's mind, and eager to join in the game with his beloved brother, took the arrow Loki had made from the mistletoe, and, guided by Loki's skilful hand, he threw it at Balder. And because the mistletoe, alone of all creatures in the world, had not taken Frigga's vow, the arrow pierced the young god's heart, and he fell down dead.

The gods were struck speechless with dismay. For a moment they could do nothing but gaze at each other and at the body of Balder, lying dead. Then when they had realised at last that this dreadful thing was really true—that Balder the young, the good, the beautiful, whom everybody in heaven and earth loved and worshipped, was dead—there arose such a weeping and wailing as never was heard before in the land of Asgard. All the gods and goddesses gathered round lamenting over the body of their favourite. Frigga wept so grievously that none could comfort her, and as for poor Höder, who in his ignorance had done the dreadful deed, he was so heart-broken that his only wish was to die too, that he might be with Balder again.

Then Hermod, another of Odin's sons, came forward and spoke to the weeping mother.

"I will ride down to the underground world," he cried, "and ask Hela, the goddess of the dead, what she will take as a ransom for Balder, that he may come back to Asgard to be our light and hope and joy again."

So, mounting Odin's own horse, which was led out for him, a wonderful steed named Sleipnir, the god said good-bye and galloped away on his sad errand.

Nine days and nights he journeyed, and at last

he reached the underground world and crossed the bridge which separated it from the land of the living. So furiously did he ride that the bridge shook beneath his horse's hoofs, and all who heard shrank back in dismay, wondering what was happening, for never before had anyone ridden into the land of the dead at such a furious pace.

Hermod found Balder sitting beside the goddess Hela, honoured by everybody. So beloved had he grown already in his new abode that Hela was very unwilling to let him go. But Hermod drew such a moving picture of the grief of Frigga and Höder, and the sorrow and mourning for Balder amongst the gods and goddesses of Asgard and the people who dwelt in the world, that at last the goddess, stern though she was, relented.

" If everything in the world, both living and life-less, weep for Balder, then I will give him up," she said. " But if one single thing refuse to weep, he shall be mine and stay with me."

Then Hermod rode back to Asgard, and if his speed had been great on his way to Hela it was a thousand times greater now. And when the gods and goddesses heard Hela's message, they went out into all the world and begged everything they found to weep for Balder. And everything in the world, men and women and trees and plants and every beast, and every living thing and every lifeless thing, wept, for there was nothing that did not love Balder for his goodness and beauty.

But as the messengers were returning to Asgard thinking that they had accomplished their mission, they found, sitting at the entrance to a cavern, an old woman, bent and withered with age, whom they had not seen before, and they begged her to weep for Balder too, that he might be given back to Asgard.

But the old woman laughed maliciously.

" What do I care for Balder ? " she said. " Let Hela keep her own ; I will not weep for him." And nothing that they said could make her change her mind. And so, because there was one thing in the world that would not weep for Balder, Hela was able to keep the young god with her in the underground world.

Afterwards it was thought that this old woman was none other than Loki himself. It was he who had caused Balder's death, and he was able to disguise himself in any form he liked. It was never known for certain, but the gods of Asgard always believed that he who had done them so much evil was the cause also of their failure to rescue Balder. And after that Loki was never allowed to enter the gates of Asgard again.

That is the story of Balder and the legend of the mistletoe. After the death of the beautiful young god things were never the same in Asgard again. For the time was coming which Odin had known from the beginning must come, when the frost giants would storm across the rainbow bridge and do battle with the gods and overcome them, only to perish themselves in the destruction which they had brought upon the world. And then would come a time of sadness and darkness and silence, which would overshadow the world for many years.

The Legend of the Mistletoe

But Odin in his all-seeing wisdom could look beyond that time of desolation and darkness, and he knew that the sadness and sorrow would not last for ever. He knew that the time would come when a new earth would arise, fresh and green and smiling, from the mists of grief and doubt, when a new sun and a new moon would be born, and peace and joy and happiness would reign in the world, when evil would be destroyed for ever, and the golden age would come once more.

And Odin knew that then Balder would be restored to the earth which mourned him so sorely, for Hela would have no power in that new world. And so he braced his heart with fortitude to endure all that was coming, looking forward through the twilight to the great and glorious dawn.

How the Wise Man Found the King

WHEN Christ was born in Bethlehem, three kings set out from their homes to find Him and worship Him. They had seen a wonderful new star in the eastern countries where they lived, and they knew that it meant that a great King was born—a King whose kingdom would never come to an end, who was mightier than the sun and greater than the stars—a King who was the Lord of earth and sky and sea.

These three kings had studied old books and prophecies, and they knew that God had promised to send this mighty King into the world one day, and when they saw the star they rejoiced with exceeding great joy. And gathering together all the richest treasures they possessed, gold and frankincense and myrrh, they set out at once to follow the guiding of the star until it led them at last to the lowly cattle shed where the Holy Child lay.

But in the country they had left there was another king. He too had studied the old prophecies with his brother-kings, and he too was waiting for some sign to tell him that the Saviour of the world had come. Something had happened to delay him when at last the star brought the glad tidings of Christ's birth. He was not ready to start with the other

358

How the Wise Man Found the King

wise men, and so he was left behind. And when he had gathered together his treasures and was ready to set out upon his journey, he was too late to follow the star that was guiding the others, and so he was obliged to find his own way as best he could across the world.

He had brought with him three jewels to give to the great King whom he was going to worship. One of them was a ruby, as red as the last rays of the setting sun. One was a sapphire, holding in its depths all the blue in sea and sky; and the third was a pearl, as pure and white as the peak of a snow-clad mountain. No money in the world was enough to buy these precious gems, so valuable were they; yet the king was ready to give them all to the God whom he was seeking.

For many long months he travelled, asking wherever he went for tidings of the other three kings. He could not catch them up; they were too far ahead for that; but by inquiring diligently of everybody he met the king managed to keep more or less upon their track.

It was a long journey and a very weary one, and the dangers and difficulties through which the other wise men had passed were ten times greater for him, all alone and unattended as he was. But his longing to reach the Christ-Child and to bow himself down in worship before Him spurred the king on. With his three jewels hidden in his bosom he rode bravely through all the dangers and surmounted all the difficulties, until at last he arrived in Judea, and knew that he could not be far from his goal.

359

As he rode through the country he heard on every side sounds of mourning and distress. Cruel Herod, frightened at what the wise men had said of the King who was born in Bethlehem, had determined to find and kill the Holy Child, lest when He grew older He should try to snatch the throne of Israel from him. So he had told the three wise men to come and tell him when they had found the Messiah, that he also might come and worship Him. But God had warned the wise men in a dream, and they had returned to their country by another way.

When Herod found that the wise men had returned to their own country another way, and did not mean to come and tell him where Christ was hidden, he sent forth an order that all the children in that part of the country under two years of age were to be killed. And the rough soldiers had gone out, and tearing the children from their mothers' arms, had killed them ruthlessly.

But there was one Child they did not kill—the one of all others that they wanted. Joseph had been warned of God in a dream, and taking the young Child and His mother, had fled with them into Egypt. And there the little family lived for many years, until Herod was dead, and it was safe for them to return to their own land again.

So when the wise man who was too late arrived at last at Bethlehem, he found that the King of the Jews whom he had come so far to worship was there no longer. He had gone, no man knew where.

The wise man was at first in despair. He had come so far and dared so much, and now it seemed

How the Wise Man Found the King

that he would never be able to offer his gifts to the King after all. Then he took heart again. Since he had come so far, what did a little farther matter? He had set out to worship the King, and he would travel through the world, if need be, until at last he found Him.

So he rode bravely on again.

He had not gone very far when he heard a woman screaming, crying bitterly for help. The king hurried to the place from where the sound came, and there he saw a poor mother with a little baby in her arms, whom a cruel soldier was trying to take from her and kill. The mother had hidden the little one safely all through the terrible massacre, and now, when she thought the danger was past, this soldier had found the child and, in spite of her prayers and cries, was about to kill it.

The king spurred forward and sprang to the ground beside the poor woman, begging the soldier to spare the little one's life. But the soldier only laughed roughly, and said that it was his duty, he must do his duty whatever happened. And again he tried to snatch the child from the woman's arms.

Then the king drew from his bosom the ruby which he was carrying to Christ. He uncovered the jewel and flashed it before the man's astonished gaze.

" I will give you this if you will spare the child's life," he said.

The soldier fixed his eyes upon the wonderful jewel, and the temptation was too great for him. He let the child and its mother go unharmed, and he himself went away with the ruby in his possession, rich beyond anything he had ever dreamed or hoped to be.

Then, a little sadly, the king rode on. He had no ruby now to offer to the Christ-Child when he found Him. Still, there were the other two jewels left. He need not be ashamed of his gifts even now, and he went on his way with renewed courage.

After many more weary months of travelling he came to a place where there was a terrible famine. The poor people were dying of sickness and hunger. They had no one to help them, and the king, overcome with pity, parted with his second jewel in order to buy food for the starving, care and comfort for the sick, and clothes and raiment for the naked. He stayed in the famine-stricken place until he had done all that he could for the poor starving people. Then he rode on again, poorer by the loss of his jewel, but rich with the blessings of those whom he had saved from death and misery.

Now the wise man had only the pearl left of all his costly offerings with which he had started on his journey. He did not regret the loss of the other two gems, for he knew that if he had had the choice over again he would still have parted with them. Only he wished, so very, very much, that he had more treasures to offer to the King.

But the pearl that was left was of even greater value than the other two jewels, and although he longed for it to be a thousand times rarer and more precious, yet he knew that it was a present fit for a king, even for the King of all the earth. And so he rode on, still seeking the Christ-Child.

How the Wise Man Found the King

Long years passed away, and the king still journeyed on, seeking the Saviour, yet never finding Him. After many years he came to a place where a poor slave girl was to be sold to a brutal master. The king tried to persuade the master to let the girl go free. But the man only laughed at him, and at last the king, finding that words were of no avail, and determined to save the poor trembling girl from the dreadful life in front of her, drew forth his last remaining jewel and bought the girl's freedom with the precious pearl, — though it went to his heart to give it away.

Then once more he started on his search, grieving that he had now no present at all to bring to the King, yet determined never to give up his quest until he had found the Lord for whom he had looked so long and faithfully.

Thirty-three years he wandered through the world, until at last, old and worn and dying, he reached Jerusalem on the very day of Our Lord's crucifixion. And there, on the Cross of Calvary, he found the King for whom he had searched so long. In spite of the cross and the crown of thorns, in spite of the scornful, mocking words of the Jews who stood around, the wise man recognised his Saviour, and he knew that he had reached the end of his journey at last. This was not the little Baby whom he had set out to seek such a long, long time ago, but still it was the King.

He pushed his way through the crowd, he sank down, exhausted, to die at the feet of his Master, and tremblingly made the confession that he had come empty-handed. He had found the great King at last, but he had nothing at all to offer Him.

But had he nothing at all ?   The legend says that Christ looked down upon the man who had searched for Him so faithfully and earnestly, and who had found Him just in time to offer the worship he had come so far to bring. *He* knew without being told why the fourth king had come empty-handed. *He* knew what had happened to the costly gifts with which he had started on his journey.   And from His Cross of suffering He spoke the tender words which took away the load from the dying man's heart :

"Inasmuch as thou hast done it unto the least of these My brethren, thou hast done it unto Me," He said, and the king knew that his long, weary journey had not been in vain.